Infinity Prime Donna Casey

"This fractal is a classic spiral, which is my favorite, and I'm always amazed at the variations and the endlessly repeating patterns that can be created out of such a primary shape." – **Donna Casey**

D1497778

Investigations
IN NUMBER, DATA, AND SPACE®

Glenview, Illinois • Boston, Massachusetts
Chandler, Arizona • Upper Saddle River, New Jersey

The Investigations curriculum was developed by TERC, Cambridge, MA.

This material is based on work supported by the National Science Foundation ("NSF") under Grant No. ESI-0095450. Any opinions, findings, and conclusions or recommendations expressed in this material are those of the author(s) and do not necessarily reflect the views of the National Science Foundation.

ISBN-13: 978-0-328-59995-0

ISBN-10: 0-328-59995-6

2 3 4 5 6 7 8 9 10 V003 14 13 12 11

T E R C

Co-Principal Investigators

Susan Jo Russell

Karen Economopoulos

Authors

Lucy Wittenberg
Director Grades 3–5

Karen Economopoulos
Director Grades K–2

Virginia Bastable
(SummerMath for Teachers,
Mt. Holyoke College)

Katie Hickey Bloomfield

Keith Cochran

Darrell Earnest

Arusha Hollister

Nancy Horowitz

Erin Leidl

Megan Murray

Young Oh

Beth W. Perry

Susan Jo Russell

Deborah Schifter
(Education
Development Center)

Kathy Sillman

Administrative Staff

Amy Taber
Project Manager

Beth Bergeron

Lorraine Brooks

Emi Fujiwara

Contributing Authors

Denise Baumann

Jennifer DiBrienza

Hollee Freeman

Paula Hooper

Jan Mokros

Stephen Monk
(University of Washington)

Mary Beth O'Connor

Judy Storeygard

Cornelia Tierney

Elizabeth Van Cleef

Carol Wright

Technology

Jim Hammerman

Classroom Field Work

Amy Appell

Rachel E. Davis

Traci Higgins

Julia Thompson

Collaborating Teachers

This group of dedicated teachers carried out extensive field testing in their classrooms, met regularly to discuss issues of teaching and learning mathematics, provided feedback to staff, welcomed staff into their classrooms to document students' work, and contributed both suggestions and written material that has been incorporated into the curriculum.

Bethany Altchek

Linda Amaral

Kimberly Beauregard

Barbara Bernard

Nancy Buell

Rose Christiansen

Chris Colbath-Hess

Lisette Colon

Kim Cook

Frances Cooper

Kathleen Drew

Rebeka Eston Salemi

Thomas Fisher

Michael Flynn

Holly Ghazey

Susan Gillis

Danielle Harrington

Elaine Herzog

Francine Hiller

Kirsten Lee Howard

Liliana Klass

Leslie Kramer

Melissa Lee Andrichak

Kelley Lee Sadowski

Jennifer Levitan

Mary Lou LoVecchio

Kristen McEnaney

Maura McGrail

Kathe Millett

Florence Molyneaux

Amy Monkiewicz

Elizabeth Monopoli

Carol Murray

Robyn Musser

Christine Norrman

Deborah O'Brien

Timothy O'Connor

Anne Marie O'Reilly

Mark Paige

Margaret Riddle

Karen Schweitzer

Elisabeth Seyferth

Susan Smith

Debra Sorvillo

Shoshanah Starr

Janice Szymaszek

Karen Tobin

JoAnn Trauschke

Ana Vaisenstein

Yvonne Watson

Michelle Woods

Mary Wright

Note: Unless otherwise noted, all contributors listed above were staff of the Education Research Collaborative at TERC during their work on the curriculum. Other affiliations during the time of development are listed.

Advisors

Deborah Lowenberg Ball,
University of Michigan

Hyman Bass, Professor of Mathematics and Mathematics Education
University of Michigan

Mary Canner, Principal, Natick Public Schools

Thomas Carpenter, Professor of Curriculum and Instruction,
University of Wisconsin-Madison

Janis Freckmann, Elementary Mathematics Coordinator,
Milwaukee Public Schools

Lynne Godfrey, Mathematics Coach,
Cambridge Public Schools

Ginger Hanlon, Instructional Specialist in Mathematics,
New York City Public Schools

DeAnn Huinker, Director, Center for Mathematics and
Science Education Research, University of Wisconsin-Milwaukee

James Kaput, Professor of Mathematics, University of
Massachusetts-Dartmouth

Kate Kline, Associate Professor, Department of Mathematics
and Statistics, Western Michigan University

Jim Lewis, Professor of Mathematics,
University of Nebraska-Lincoln

William McCallum, Professor of Mathematics,
University of Arizona

Harriet Pollatsek, Professor of Mathematics,
Mount Holyoke College

Debra Shein-Gerson, Elementary Mathematics Specialist,
Weston Public Schools

Gary Shevell, Assistant Principal,
New York City Public Schools

Liz Sweeney, Elementary Math Department,
Boston Public Schools

Lucy West, Consultant, Metamorphosis:
Teaching Learning Communities, Inc.

This revision of the curriculum was built on the work of the many authors who contributed to the first edition (published between 1994 and 1998). We acknowledge the critical contributions of these authors in developing the content and pedagogy of *Investigations*:

Authors

Joan Akers

Michael T. Battista

Douglas H. Clements

Karen Economopoulos

Marlene Kliman

Jan Mokros

Megan Murray

Ricardo Nemirovsky

Andee Rubin

Susan Jo Russell

Cornelia Tierney

Contributing Authors

Mary Berle-Carman

Rebecca B. Corwin

Rebeka Eston

Claryce Evans

Anne Goodrow

Cliff Konold

Chris Mainhart

Sue McMillen

Jerrie Moffet

Tracy Noble

Kim O'Neil

Mark Ogonowski

Julie Sarama

Amy Shulman Weinberg

Margie Singer

Virginia Woolley

Tracey Wright

Contents

UNIT 1

Who Is in School Today?

Investigations

Overview of Program Components

The **Curriculum Units** are the teaching guides. (See far right.)

Implementing Investigations in Kindergarten offers suggestions for implementing the curriculum. It also contains a comprehensive index.

Investigations for the Interactive Whiteboard provides whole-class instructional support to enhance each session.

The **Resource Masters CD** contains all reproducible materials that support instruction.
The **Shapes CD** provides an environment in which students investigate a variety of geometric ideas.

The **Student Activity Book** contains the consumable student pages (Recording Sheets, Homework, Practice, and so on).

The **Student Math Handbook Flip Chart** contains pictures of Math Words and Ideas pages.

The *Investigations* Curriculum

Investigations in Number, Data, and Space® is a K–5 mathematics curriculum designed to engage students in making sense of mathematical ideas. Six major goals guided the development of the *Investigations in Number, Data, and Space®* curriculum. The curriculum is designed to:

- Support students to make sense of mathematics and learn that they can be mathematical thinkers

- Focus on computational fluency with whole numbers as a major goal of the elementary grades

- Provide substantive work in important areas of mathematics—rational numbers, geometry, measurement, data, and early algebra—and connections among them

- Emphasize reasoning about mathematical ideas

- Communicate mathematics content and pedagogy to teachers

- Engage the range of learners in understanding mathematics

Underlying these goals are three guiding principles that are touchstones for the *Investigations* team as we approach both students and teachers as agents of their own learning:

1. *Students have mathematical ideas.* Students come to school with ideas about numbers, shapes, measurements, patterns, and data. If given the opportunity to learn in an environment that stresses making sense of mathematics, students build on the ideas they already have and learn about new mathematics they have never encountered. Students learn that they are capable of having mathematical ideas, applying what they know to new situations, and thinking and reasoning about unfamiliar problems.

2. *Teachers are engaged in ongoing learning* about mathematics content, pedagogy, and student learning. The curriculum provides material for professional development, to be used by teachers individually or in groups, that supports teachers' continued learning as they use the curriculum over several years. The *Investigations* curriculum materials are designed as much to be a dialogue with teachers as to be a core of content for students.

3. *Teachers collaborate with the students and curriculum materials* to create the curriculum as enacted in the classroom. The only way for a good curriculum to be used well is for teachers to be active participants in implementing it. Teachers use the curriculum to maintain a clear, focused, and coherent agenda for mathematics teaching. At the same time, they observe and listen carefully to students, try to understand how they are thinking, and make teaching decisions based on these observations.

Investigations is based on experience from research and practice, including field testing that involved documentation of thousands of hours in classrooms, observations of students, input from teachers, and analysis of student work. As a result, the curriculum addresses the learning needs of real students in a wide range of classrooms and communities. The investigations are carefully designed to invite all students into mathematics—girls and boys; members of diverse cultural, ethnic, and language groups; and students with a wide variety of strengths, needs, and interests.

Based on this extensive classroom testing, the curriculum takes seriously the time students need to develop a strong conceptual foundation and skills based on that foundation. Each curriculum unit focuses on an area of content in depth, providing time for students to develop and practice ideas across a variety of activities and contexts that build on each other. Daily guidelines for time spent on class sessions, Classroom Routines (K–3), and Ten-Minute Math (3–5) reflect the commitment to devoting adequate time to mathematics in each school day.

About This Curriculum Unit

This **Curriculum Unit** is one of seven teaching guides in Grade K. The first unit in Grade K is *Who Is in School Today?*

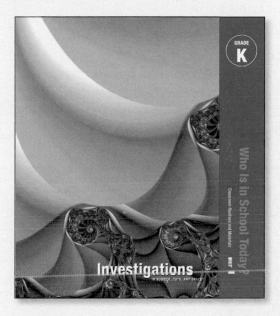

- The **Introduction and Overview** section organizes and presents the instructional materials, provides background information, and highlights important features specific to this unit.

- Each Curriculum Unit contains several **Investigations.** Each Investigation focuses on a set of related mathematical ideas.

- Investigations are divided into 30–45 minute **Sessions,** or lessons.

- Sessions have a combination of these parts: **Activity, Discussion, Math Workshop,** and **Session Follow-Up.**

- Each session also has one or more **Classroom Routines** that are done outside of math time.

- At the back of the book is a collection of **Teacher Notes** and **Dialogue Boxes** that provide professional development related to the unit.

- Also included at the back of the book are the **Student Math Handbook Flip Chart** pages for this unit.

- The **Index** provides a way to look up important words or terms.

Overview

OF THIS UNIT

Each *Investigations* session has some combination of these five parts: **Activity, Discussion, Math Workshop, Assessment,** and **Session Follow-Up.** These session parts are indicated in the chart below. Each session also has one **Classroom Routine** that is done outside of math time.

 (W) Interactive Whiteboard

Classroom Routines

Activity	Discussion	Math Workshop	Assessment Checklist*	Session Follow-Up		Calendar	Attendance
(W)●	●	(W)		●			
(W)	●	●		●			
●	●	(W)		●			(W)
●	●	(W)		●			(W)
	(W)	●		●		(W)	
(W)●	●	●		●		(W)	
(W)	●	(W)	●	●		(W)	
(W)	(W)	●		●		(W)	
(W)	●	●		●			(W)
(W)	●	●		●			(W)
(W)	●	●		●		(W)	
(W)	●	●		●			(W)
(W)	●	●		●		(W)	
●	●	(W)		●			(W)
(W)(W)	●	●		●		(W)	
●	(W)	●		●			(W)
●	●	(W)		●		(W)	
●	●	(W)		●			(W)

*An Assessment Checklist is introduced in this session.

Mathematics

IN THIS UNIT

Who Is In School Today? is the first of seven units in the Kindergarten sequence. The main focus of this unit is to establish a mathematical community. Therefore, this unit introduces the processes (e.g., using and caring for materials), structures (e.g., Math Workshop), and materials (e.g., pattern blocks) that will be important features of math class this year. It also introduces routines common to many Kindergarten classrooms that students will regularly encounter throughout the year: taking attendance, using the calendar to count and keep track of time and events, counting sets of objects, and collecting and discussing data about the class.

Exploring materials in this unit will help students develop language to describe attributes, such as color, size, shape; quantity and position; and serves as an introduction to sorting.

This unit is an introduction to the mathematical content, materials, processes, and ways of working that students will use throughout the year in the *Investigations* curriculum. As they are introduced to four Classroom Routines that they will do regularly over the course of the year and as they explore materials, students will:

- Become familiar with the expectations for learning

- Explore some of the materials that they will be using to model mathematical situations and solve mathematical problems

- Talk about mathematical problems and share solution strategies

- Work with peers as they share ideas and materials

- Rely on their own thinking and learn from the thinking of others

LOOKING BACK This unit is designed to meet the needs of the range of learners entering Kindergarten as 5-year-olds.

This unit focuses on 4 Mathematical Emphases:

1 Counting and Quantity Developing strategies for accurately counting a set of objects by 1s

Math Focus Points

- ◆ Counting the number of students in the class

- ◆ Using the calendar to count days

- ◆ Connecting number names, numerals, and quantities

- ◆ Establishing one-to-one correspondence between equal groups (e.g., students and cubes)

- ◆ Developing strategies for accurately counting and keeping track of quantities up to the number of students in the class

- ◆ Creating an equivalent set

- ◆ Counting, creating, and representing quantities

Number concepts are central to each of the yearlong activities introduced in this unit: *Attendance, Calendar,* Counting Jar, and *Today's Question.* Each involves counting and provides a chance to compare quantities with terms, such as more, less, and the same. Students count themselves and their classmates, the days on the calendar, a set of objects in a jar, and names on a chart. In addition to counting a given set, students are asked to create a set of a given size and eventually to represent a quantity on paper.

Although many kindergarteners can recite some portion of the "counting song," many have minimal experience with the counting sequence or the process of counting. Because young children learn how to count by having many opportunities to count and to see and hear others count, and because much of the counting in this unit focuses on a number that is quite large for beginning-of-the-year kindergarteners (i.e., the number of students in the class), much of the counting happens in the whole group; students counting along with you as high as they are able. There are several reasons for the focus on a relatively large number. Practically, teachers are required to take attendance and most involve students in this process. More importantly, a critical part of establishing a classroom community is getting to know one another. Finally, this number will play an important mathematical role this year, as many activities involve data about the class. As students think about who is here and who is not, and eventually, *how many* are here and *how many* are not (and how they know), they begin to consider part-whole relationships, such as the relationship between the number present, the number absent, and the total number of students in the class.

The class counts around the circle.

When they count sets on their own, the numbers are quite small so that students can focus on learning the sequence and other important aspects of counting—giving one number to each object, counting each object once and only once, keeping track of what has been counted and what remains to be counted, seeing that the last number said represents the total number counted, and so on.

2 Data Analysis Sorting and Classifying

Math Focus Points

◆ Identifying attributes (e.g., color, size, and shape) and developing language to describe them

◆ Comparing how objects are the same and different

◆ Finding objects that share one attribute

◆ Using attributes to sort a group of objects

Identifying attributes of objects—and using attributes to sort and classify them—is essential to the study of mathematics, particularly data and geometry. Students' first exposure to thinking about attributes comes as they explore materials like pattern blocks, Geoblocks, connecting cubes, color tiles, buttons, and attribute blocks. These manipulatives provide many attributes to consider, such as color, shape, size, material (e.g., wood or plastic), thickness, number of holes, function, and so on.

After such materials are explored, matching and sorting activities follow. They build on kindergarteners' natural interest in thinking about how things are the same and different. Students must identify an attribute of one person or object (e.g., a button) in order to find another that shares at least one attribute (e.g., two holes), or students sort a set of people or attribute blocks into two groups (e.g., children who are wearing sneakers and children who are not wearing sneakers). As students look for similarities among people or objects, they begin to see how two objects can be the same in some ways and different in others.

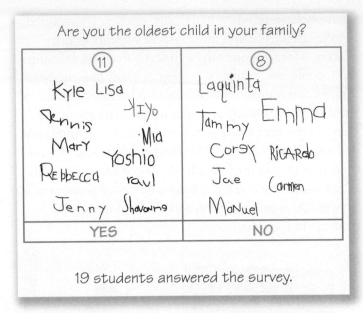

Are you the oldest child in your family?

⑪	⑧
Kyle Lisa Kiyo Dennis Mia Mary Yoshio Rebbecca raul Jenny Shavonne	Laquinta Emma Tammy Corey Ricardo Jae Carmen Manuel
YES	NO

19 students answered the survey.

3 Data Analysis Carrying out a data investigation

Math Focus Points

◆ Collecting and keeping track of survey data

◆ Describing and comparing the number of pieces of data in each category

◆ Interpreting results of a data investigation

It is important that elementary students have the opportunity to experience the many aspects of carrying out a data investigation—collecting, recording, representing, describing, and interpreting data. In this unit, students are introduced to *Today's Question*. This routine asks students to respond to a survey question and analyze the results by thinking about questions, such as:

• How many people said, "Yes"?

• How many people said, "No"?

• Which group has more?

• How many people responded to the survey?

• What did we learn about our class from this survey?

Because it includes questions that help classmates get to know one another, this activity also serves the goal of developing a classroom community.

Students also collect, count, represent, and interpret data about themselves as they take attendance. While determining how many students are here or not here or how many girls and how many boys are in the class, they count and compare quantities that have real meaning to them. As they analyze the two groups, they consider which is more and which is less and explore part-part-whole relationships (e.g., the relationship between the number of girls, the number of boys, and the total number of students).

4 Whole Number Operations Using manipulatives, drawings, tools, and notation to show strategies and solutions

Math Focus Points

◆ Exploring math manipulatives and their attributes

◆ Using the calendar as a tool for keeping track of time and events

◆ Representing quantities with pictures, numbers, objects, and/or words

Throughout the year, students use manipulatives to solve problems, model their thinking, and show their solutions. Because young children need to be familiar with such tools in order to use them effectively, this unit asks students to explore a variety of materials. As they do so, students discover and explore important attributes (e.g., color, size, and shape) and relationships (e.g., You can use two red trapezoid pattern blocks to make a shape the same size and shape as the yellow hexagon.) that will prepare them to use such materials in more structured and focused ways later in the year.

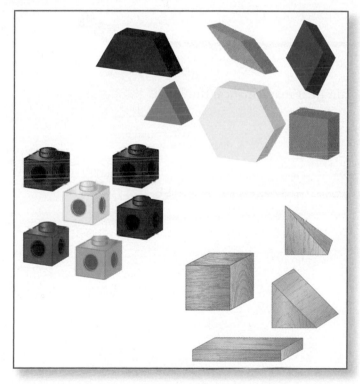

Students need many and varied experiences with representing quantities as they develop an understanding of counting, quantity, and representation. In the *Attendance* routine, students make a cube tower that represents the total number of students in the class. The Counting Jar asks students to represent a quantity—first with manipulatives and later on paper.

This Unit also focuses on

◆ Developing language to describe shapes, position, and quantity

Classroom Routines focus on

◆ Developing strategies for counting accurately

◆ Considering whether order matters when you count

◆ Comparing quantities

◆ Using the calendar as a tool for keeping track of time

◆ Collecting, counting, representing, describing, and comparing data

LOOKING FORWARD The work in this unit lays the foundation for subsequent units in the Kindergarten sequence. The Classroom Routines are revisited in every unit and vary as students' mathematical understandings grow and deepen. Students use the manipulatives they explored in this unit in more focused ways as they solve problems and represent solutions throughout the year. Students' work with attributes and sorting is revisited and extended in *Make a Shape, Build a Block* (Unit 5) and *Sorting and Surveys* (Unit 7).

Assessment

IN THIS UNIT

Every session in this unit provides an opportunity for Ongoing Assessment. In addition, assessment checklists are provided to keep track of your observations about students' work with concepts and ideas that are benchmarks for this unit.

ONGOING ASSESSMENT: Observing Students at Work

The following sessions provide **Ongoing Assessment: Observing Students at Work** opportunities:

- **Session 1.1, pp. 28, 29, and 30**
- **Session 1.6, pp. 50 and 51**
- **Session 2.1, p. 61**
- **Session 2.3, p. 73**
- **Session 2.4, p. 79**
- **Session 3.1, p. 96**
- **Session 3.2, p. 103**
- **Session 3.4, p. 112**

WRITING OPPORTUNITIES

The following sessions have **writing** opportunities for students to explain their mathematical thinking:

- **Session 3.1, p. 96**
  Today's Question
- **Sessions 3.2–3.6, pp. 101–102, 108, 113, 117, 122**
  Counting Jar

PORTFOLIO OPPORTUNITIES

The following sessions have work appropriate for a **portfolio:**

- **Sessions 3.2–3.6, pp. 101–102, 108, 113, 117, 122**
  Counting Jar

Assessing the Benchmarks

Throughout the Kindergarten curriculum, observing students' work and engaging them in conversation about their ideas are primary means of assessing their mathematical understanding. Every unit subsequent to this one highlights specific activities to observe (assessment activities), offers questions to consider as you watch students at work, provides charts for keeping track of your observations, and describes what is expected of students (benchmarks).

This unit is different because it is the first unit of the Kindergarten year. It is designed to introduce students to school and to mathematics, and to provide the teacher with many opportunities to get to know students, assess where they are mathematically, establish routines and expectations that support learning, develop processes and set up structures that students will use all year, encourage students to work on problems in ways that make sense to them, and communicate their interest in and respect for students' mathematical ideas.

Although there are no mathematical expectations or benchmarks in this unit, a tool for keeping track of your initial observations about students' counting skills is introduced in Session 2.1, page 60. Examples of how teachers use this tool are included in Sessions 2.1 and 3.2, pages 61 and 104. Information about how students learn to count fluently is included in **Teacher Notes:** Counting Is More Than 1, 2, 3, page 127 and Observing Kindergarteners as They Count, page 135.

Classroom Routines

Classroom Routines offer practice and review of key concepts for this grade level. These daily activities, to be done in 10 minutes outside of math class, occur in a regular rotation every 4–5 days. Specific directions for the day's routine are provided in each session. For a full description and variations of each classroom routine see *Implementing Investigations in Kindergarten.*

Attendance

Students count to determine the total number of students present and to explore what happens when the count begins with different students. In order to help students connect the counting numbers to the quantities they represent, the class discusses how many students have been counted midway through the count. Students also compare two groups, determine which group has more, and decide how many more there are in the larger group.

Math Focus Points

◆ Developing strategies for counting accurately

◆ Considering whether order matters when you count

◆ Comparing quantities

Calendar

Students review the numbers and counting sequence to 31 and the names and sequence of the days of the week. Students also use the calendar to determine how many days until (or since) a special event and explain their strategies.

Math Focus Points

◆ Using the calendar as a tool for keeping track of time

◆ Developing strategies for counting accurately

Today's Question

Students record their response to a survey question with two possible answers on a two-column table. Class discussion focuses on describing and interpreting the data.

Math Focus Points

◆ Collecting, counting, representing, describing, and comparing data

Practice and Review

Practice and review play a critical role in the *Investigations* program. The following components and features are available to provide regular reinforcement of key mathematical concepts and procedures.

Books	Features	In This Unit . . .
Curriculum Unit	**Classroom Routines** offer practice and review of key concepts for this grade level. These daily activities, to be done in ten minutes outside of math class, occur in a regular rotation every 4–5 days. Specific directions for the day's routine are provided in each session. For the full description and variations of each classroom routine see *Implementing Investigations in Kindergarten*.	• **Each session after 1.2**
Student Activity Book	**Practice** pages in the *Student Activity Book* provide one of two types of written practice: **reinforcement** of the content of the unit or **enrichment** opportunities.	• **Session 1.5** • **Session 2.3** • **Session 2.5** • **Session 3.6**
	Homework pages in the *Student Activity Book* are an extension of the work done in class. At times they help students prepare for upcoming activities.	• **No Sessions**
Student Math Handbook Flip Chart	**Math Words and Ideas** in the *Student Math Handbook Flip Chart* are pages that summarize key words and ideas. Most Words and Ideas pages have at least one exercise.	• **Student Math Handbook Flip Chart, pp. 4–10, 15–18, 20, 44, 47–49**

Supporting the Range of Learners

Sessions	1.1	1.2	2.1	2.3	2.4	2.5	3.1	3.2	3.4	3.5
Intervention	●		●	●	●		●	●	●	
Extension					●	●		●		●
ELL	●	●		●					●	

Intervention

Suggestions are made to support and engage students who are having difficulty with a particular idea, activity, or problem.

Extension

Suggestions are made to support and engage students who finish early or may be ready for additional challenge.

English Language Learners (ELL)

In this introductory unit, English Language Learners will encounter many new words, language structures, and concepts. You can assist their learning by reinforcing key content one-on-one or in a small group, by offering ample visual support, and by providing repeated opportunities for students to hear and use math-related language in meaningful contexts.

Although the repetition of the daily routines will support English Language Learners' learning, it may be helpful to preview and/or review some routines in a small group

setting, where you can more effectively assess students' understanding. English Language Learners will benefit from extra reinforcement of the *Calendar* routine, as the words for *day, week, month,* and *year* may be unfamiliar to them, along with the names for days of the week and for months of the year in English. When you look at the calendar together, try to link it as much as possible to the students' lives.

Working with the Range of Learners: Classroom Cases is a set of episodes written by teachers that focuses on meeting the needs of the range of learners in the classroom. In the first section, *Setting up the Mathematical Community,* teachers write about how they create a supportive and productive learning environment in their classrooms. In the next section, *Accommodations for Learning,* teachers focus on specific modifications they make to meet the needs of some of their learners. In the last section, *Language and Representation,* teachers share how they help students use representations and develop language to investigate and express mathematical ideas. The questions at the end of each case provide a starting point for your own reflection or for discussion with colleagues. See *Implementing Investigations in Kindergarten* for this set of episodes.

Mathematical Emphases

Counting and Quantity Developing strategies for accurately counting a set of objects by 1s

Math Focus Points

◆ Counting the number of students in the class

◆ Using the calendar to count days

◆ Connecting number names, numerals, and quantities

◆ Establishing one-to-one correspondence between equal groups (e.g., students and cubes)

Whole Number Operations Using manipulatives, drawings, tools, and notation to show strategies and solutions

Math Focus Points

◆ Exploring math manipulatives and their attributes

◆ Using the calendar as a tool for keeping track of time and events

This Investigation also focuses on

◆ Developing language to describe shapes, position, and quantity

The Attendance and Calendar Routines

SESSION 1.1 p. 24	Student Activity Book	Student Math Handbook Flip Chart	Professional Development: Read Ahead of Time	
The Attendance Routine: How Many Are We? After discussing the purpose and reason for taking attendance, the class counts to establish the number of students in their class. Then, students are introduced to and explore math materials that they will use all year long—pattern blocks, Geoblocks, and connecting cubes.		17, 18	• **Mathematics in This Unit,** p. 10 • **Part 4: Classroom Routines** in *Implementing Investigations in Kindergarten:* Attendance • **Teacher Notes:** Counting Is More Than 1, 2, 3, p. 127; Supporting Students' Free Play, p. 132; About Pattern Blocks, p. 128; About Geoblocks, p. 129 • **Part 2: Using** *Investigations* in *Implementing Investigations in Kindergarten:* Setting Up the *Investigations* Classroom • **Dialogue Box:** Flowers, Dancers, and Pattern-Block Walls, p. 137	
SESSION 1.2 p. 32				
Attendance: Counting Around the Circle Students revisit the *Attendance* Routine, counting the number of students in two different ways. Math Workshop continues to focus on the exploration of math materials.			• **Dialogue Box:** I'm Not 8, I'm 5!, p. 139 • **Teacher Note:** Exploring Materials: Introducing Math Vocabulary, p. 134	
SESSION 1.3 p. 36				
The Calendar Routine Students are introduced to a classroom routine focused on the calendar—a tool for keeping track of time and events. Math Workshop continues to focus on the exploration of math materials.		15	• **Part 4: Classroom Routines** in *Implementing Investigations in Kindergarten:* Calendar • **Dialogue Box:** What's a Calendar?, p. 140	

Classroom Routines See page 16 for an overview.

Attendance
- Name tags
- Attendance Recording Sheet

Calendar
- Pocket calendar
- "Today" marker

Materials to Gather	Materials to Prepare
• **Chart paper** (1 sheet; optional) • **Pattern blocks** (1 set per 4–6 students) • **Set of other building blocks** (optional) • **Tray or sturdy cardboard work mat** (1 per student)	• **Name tags** Print each student's name on a 4 x 6 index card. If possible, include photo of child. (1 per student) • **Attendance Recording Sheet** Make a sheet for recording each day's attendance data and laminate it. Include on the sheet: "We have _____ students in our class. _____ students are here today. _____ students are absent." See page 26. • **Geoblocks** Divide each class set into two equivalent sets. • **Connecting cubes** Divide the class set into 4–5 bins.
• **Materials for *Attendance*** See Session 1.1. • **Materials for Exploring Pattern Blocks** See Session 1.1. • **Materials for Exploring Geoblocks** See Session 1.1. • **Materials for Exploring Connecting Cubes** See Session 1.1.	• **M1–M2, Family Letter** Make copies. (1 per student)
• **Pocket calendar with removable numbers** • **Several types of calendars** (e.g., datebooks, yearlong wall calendars; optional) • **Materials for Exploring Pattern Blocks** See Session 1.1. • **Materials for Exploring Geoblocks** See Session 1.1. • **Materials for Exploring Connecting Cubes** See Session 1.1.	• **"Today" marker** Create a marker or tag to show which day it is on the calendar. See page 39.

The Attendance and Calendar Routines, *continued*

	Student Activity Book	Student Math Handbook Flip Chart	Professional Development: Read Ahead of Time	
SESSION 1.4 p. 41				
Calendar: Adding Special Days Students count to figure out today's date, and to find the dates of special events to be placed on the class calendar. Math Workshop continues to focus on the exploration of math materials.		15, 16		
SESSION 1.5 p. 44				
Comparing Materials Math Workshop continues to focus on the exploration of math materials. Class discussion focuses on comparing the different materials students have been exploring.	1			
SESSION 1.6 p. 47				
Making an Attendance Stick The class counts the number of students in two different ways and then uses connecting cubes to create a tower that represents the total number of students in the class. Then, they are introduced to more math materials they will use this year—square tiles, attribute blocks, and buttons.		17, 18		

Materials to Gather	Materials to Prepare
• **Pocket Calendar with removable numbers** See Session 1.3. • **Materials for Exploring Pattern Blocks** See Session 1.1. • **Materials for Exploring Geoblocks** See Session 1.1. • **Materials for Exploring Connecting Cubes** See Session 1.1.	• **"Special Day" markers** Create markers that will fit in the pocket calendar that illustrate special events. (e.g., field trips, students' birthdays, visitors, school celebrations, holidays, days off.) See page 42.
• **Pattern blocks** (1 set) • **Geoblocks** (1 subset) • **Connecting cubes** (1 bin) • **Materials for Exploring Pattern Blocks** See Session 1.1. • **Materials for Exploring Geoblocks** See Session 1.1. • **Materials for Exploring Connecting Cubes** See Session 1.1.	
• **Materials for** *Attendance* See Session 1.1. • **Tray or sturdy cardboard work mat** (1 per student; optional)	• **Connecting cubes** Put as many cubes in a bin as there are students in the class. Use cubes of the same color. • **Color tiles** Divide the class set into smaller containers. (1 bucket per every 4–6 students) • **Buttons** Divide the class set into smaller containers. (1 bin per small group) • **Attribute blocks** Split each set in half, creating a thick and thin set. (1 subset per pair)

The Attendance Routine: How Many Are We?

Math Focus Points

◆ Counting the number of students in the class

◆ Exploring math manipulatives and their attributes

◆ Developing language to describe shapes, position, and quantity

Vocabulary

taking attendance

Today's Plan		Materials
① ACTIVITY **Introducing** *Attendance* 5–10 MIN · CLASS		• Name tags*; Attendance Recording Sheet*; chart paper (optional)
② ACTIVITY **Introducing Math Workshop and Materials** 5–10 MIN · CLASS		• Pattern blocks; Geoblocks*; connecting cubes*; set of other building blocks (optional); tray or sturdy cardboard work mat
③ MATH WORKSHOP **Exploring Materials** **3A Exploring Pattern Blocks** **3B Exploring Geoblocks** **3C Exploring Connecting Cubes** 15–20 MIN		**3A** • Pattern blocks; tray or sturdy cardboard work mat (optional) **3B** • Geoblocks; other building blocks (optional); tray or sturdy cardboard work mat **3C** • Connecting cubes
④ DISCUSSION **Checking In** 5 MIN · CLASS		
⑤ SESSION FOLLOW-UP **Practice**		• *Student Math Handbook Flip Chart,* pp. 17, 18

*See *Materials to Prepare,* p. 21.

Classroom Routines

Attendance The *Attendance* routine is introduced in this session, so it will not be done outside of math time.

ACTIVITY

Introducing *Attendance*

5–10 MIN · CLASS

Gather students in a meeting area where they can see you and each other—ideally seated in a circle or semicircle.

I'd like you to look carefully around our circle. These are the people in our class this year. Every day when we come to school, we need to see if everyone is here. This is called taking attendance. Some days you might not come to school because you're sick. So, every day we'll need to figure out who is here and who is not here. Why do you think it is important for us to take attendance every day?❶

Encourage students to share their ideas.

Every day we need to figure out how many children are here and not here. Look around the circle. How could we figure out how many kids are here today?

Some students may tell you to count the children. Others may suggest that a student do this or offer to do it themselves. Because this is the first time counting the students in the class, model the process. Go around the circle and say one number as you point to each child. Encourage students to count together with you.

I'm going to go around the circle and point to each person as I count all of you. See if you can help me as I count the number of people in our class.

Counting as a group often helps students go further in the counting sequence than they could go on their own.❷ Don't be surprised or concerned if you are the only one saying the ending numbers.❸

Show students the name tags that you created and explain that there is one for each member of the class. Then hold up the name tags of absent students and determine the total number of students in the class.❹

We counted each person in the circle and found out that there are 23 students here today. But we know that [Tammy] and [Victor] [hold up their name tags] are *not here* today. When everyone is here, there will be 25 children in our class.

Teaching Notes

❶ **The *Attendance* Routine** The basic version of this activity and its variations, which unfold over the course of this investigation, are suggested over the course of the year and provide regular practice with counting and reasoning about the number of students in the class. Adapt this routine to connect it to your school's method for reporting attendance (e.g., an attendance sheet or log book). For a full write-up, see **Part 4: Classroom Routines** in *Implementing Investigations in Kindergarten: Attendance*

❹ **How Many Are We?** The number of students in the class is important; it plays a role throughout the school year. Regardless of class size, students develop a good sense of this number as they count each member and as they think about its different combinations (the number of girls and boys, the number present and absent, and so on).

Math Note

❷ **Learning to Count** Although many kindergarteners can recite some portion of the counting sequence or "counting song" and a few may be able to count the total number of students in the class, many have minimal experience with counting. Students learn the counting sequence and how to count by having many opportunities to count and to see others count.

Professional Development

❸ **Teacher Note:** Counting Is More Than 1, 2, 3, p. 127

Professional Development

⑤ **Part 2: Using** *Investigations* in *Implementing Investigations in Kindergarten.*

Teaching Notes

⑥ **Work Mats** If space is an issue or materials are limited, trays or mats can help define the space and limit the amount of materials students can use. They also provide a way for students to bring completed work to the meeting area.

Once you have established the total number of students in your class and the number present and absent today, fill in the information on your Attendance Recording Sheet or record it on the board or on chart paper.

> We have _25_ students in our class.
>
> _23_ students are here today.
>
> _2_ students are absent.

ACTIVITY

5–10 MIN **CLASS**

② Introducing Math Workshop and Materials

Briefly explain what Math Workshop is and how it will work in your class.⑤

Every day that we have school, we will have math. On many of those days, we will have something called Math Workshop. During Math Workshop, there will be several activities that you can choose to do.

Show students a bin of connecting cubes, a set of pattern blocks, a subset of Geoblocks, and—if students are to use them—a tray or cardboard mat.⑥ Then briefly introduce these materials.

Containers of connecting cubes, pattern blocks, and Geoblocks are ready for students to use in Math Workshop.

We will use lots of different tools to solve math problems and play math games this year. These are a few of the tools. They are connecting cubes, pattern blocks, and Geoblocks.

Ask if students are familiar with any of the materials and how they have used them in the past.

During Math Workshop today, and every day for the next few weeks, you are going to have time to explore these math materials.❼

With the introduction of any new material, it is important to establish clear ground rules. Show students where the materials are stored and be sure to discuss how students should use, share, and care for them.❽

We don't have enough Geoblocks, pattern blocks, and connecting cubes for everyone to use them all at once, so you will have to take turns. If you don't get a chance to use the material you want today, please don't worry. They will be part of Math Workshop for a long time.❾

Explain that each material—or center, if you have set your room up this way—can accommodate a specific number of students. Depending on how you have organized your classroom, this could be indicated by the number of chairs at a certain table or by posting the information on a Math Workshop Board.

MATH WORKSHOP

15–20 MIN

③ Exploring Materials

Use the following questions to gather information about how students make choices and involve themselves with activities.❿

- Do students stick with the same material for a period of time or do they move quickly from activity to activity?

- Do students work alone, in pairs, or in small groups? Are they able to share materials, space, and ideas? Are they interested in the work of others?

Help students choose among the following three activities and get started.

- Exploring pattern blocks

- Exploring Geoblocks

- Exploring connecting cubes

Teaching Notes

⑪ **Transitions** Approximately ten minutes before the end-of-session discussion, let students know they have about five minutes left to work. After about five minutes, ask students to clean up their materials, check the floor for any stray cubes or blocks, and return the materials to their containers. Alerting students to such transitions can help them proceed more smoothly.

⑭ **Naming Shapes** Kindergarteners are not expected to use formal terms for the shapes in these sets.

DIFFERENTIATION: Supporting the Range of Learners

Intervention Help students structure and focus their explorations as needed.⑪

ELL By observing English Language Learners as they explore the math materials, you can begin to assess how familiar they are with English words related to attributes such as color, size, and shape. English Language Learners will learn much of this language indirectly as they interact with their classmates during Math Workshop. You can introduce and reinforce key vocabulary by engaging students in informal conversation about their work.

3A Exploring Pattern Blocks

INDIVIDUALS PAIRS GROUPS

Students explore pattern blocks—a set of flat blocks that includes six shapes. These blocks are useful for pattern-making, counting, sorting, and geometry activities.⑫

ONGOING ASSESSMENT: Observing Students at Work

Students explore pattern blocks and their attributes.

- **How do students use pattern blocks?** Do they lay them flat? Stand them on edge? Build vertically or stack them? What do they create (e.g., designs, patterns, pictures, towers)?

- **How do students describe pattern-block constructions?** Do they have language to describe the position of different blocks (e.g., above/below, in front of/behind, next to/near)?

- **How do they describe individual pattern blocks?** Do they refer to them by color? Size? Shape? What language do they use?⑬ ⑭

- **What do students discover about pattern blocks?** Do they see that some blocks "fit together" or that they can substitute some blocks for others (e.g., 2 red trapezoids for a yellow hexagon)?

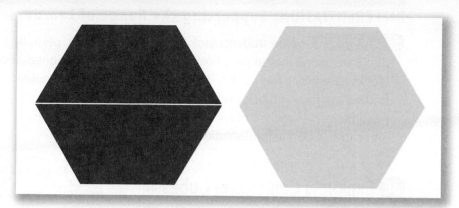

③B Exploring Geoblocks

 INDIVIDUALS   PAIRS   GROUPS

Students explore Geoblocks—a set of three-dimensional wooden blocks useful for geometry, sorting, pattern-making, and counting activities.⑮

ONGOING ASSESSMENT: Observing Students at Work

Observe students as they explore Geoblocks and their attributes.

- **How do students use Geoblocks? What do they make?** Do they stack the blocks vertically? Build horizontally, covering space? Use them for dramatic play? (e.g., One group thought of the tiny cubes as "gold" and stored them in a box made of prisms.)

- **How do students describe Geoblock constructions?** Do they have language to describe the position of different blocks (e.g., above/below, in front of/behind, next to/near)?

- **How do students describe individual Geoblocks?** Do they refer to size? (e.g., "I need one that's littler.") Overall shape and function? (e.g., "Can I have that ramp?") Other geometric attributes (e.g., "the very pointy one" or "the one with the triangle")? What words do they use?

- **What do students discover about Geoblocks?** Do they notice that the faces (sides) are squares, rectangles, and triangles or that combinations of blocks can be substituted for other blocks?

Teaching Notes

16 Connecting Cubes These small cubes come in a variety of colors. Any side of a cube can link to any side of another. This is one of their most important features because it allows students to build three-dimensional constructions. Connecting cubes are used throughout the year to count, make patterns, and model and represent problems.

17 Saving Constructions Students often want to save the things they make with blocks or cubes. Depending on the size of your class and the supply of materials you have, you can develop a saving policy. Students often suggest that things be saved for as long as a week, but quickly vote for a change when they see that there are very few materials left to use after only a few days. Most teachers say that keeping constructions intact for one day seems to satisfy students' needs to save and share.

DIFFERENTIATION: Supporting the Range of Learners

Intervention Some students look for a particular block, perhaps a duplicate of one they already have. The way the set is designed, several blocks have only a few copies. When students are having trouble finding a particular block, encourage them to think about other possible ways to make a block that is the same size and shape. This can also be a helpful solution for resolving sharing issues.

3C Exploring Connecting Cubes

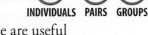

INDIVIDUALS PAIRS GROUPS

Students freely explore connecting cubes. These are useful for pattern-making and counting activities and for making three-dimensional constructions.**16**

Students explore connecting cubes.

ONGOING ASSESSMENT: Observing Students at Work

Students explore connecting cubes and their attributes.**17**

- **How do students use connecting cubes?** Do they keep them loose or link them together? What do they make with them? Do they make long rods or trains? Do their constructions capitalize on the interlocking feature?

- **How do students describe the cubes and their creations?** Do they have language to describe the position of different cubes (e.g., above/below, in front of/behind, next to/near)?

DIFFERENTIATION: Supporting the Range of Learners

Intervention Manipulating connecting cubes, particularly if the set is quite new, can be challenging for small hands. Some students may need help snapping or unsnapping them.

DISCUSSION

4 Checking In

5 MIN   CLASS

Take this opportunity to discuss any issues that you have noticed while observing students at work.⑱ Because Math Workshop will be an integral part of math this year, many of the discussions over the first few weeks are likely to focus on logistics and management. Topics might include the following:

- The number of students that each activity can accommodate

- Using and sharing materials

- Caring for and storing materials

- Noise level

- Making choices

- Working with a partner or group

- Working purposefully

For example, if sharing materials is a problem, have students role-play the situation and brainstorm strategies for dealing with it. Discuss what works and what does not work or point out how one pair worked out a fair solution to a problem.

SESSION FOLLOW-UP

5 Practice

Student Math Handbook Flip Chart: Use the *Student Math Handbook Flip Chart* pages 17, 18 to reinforce concepts from today's session. See pages 144–148 in the back of this unit.

Attendance: Counting Around the Circle

Math Focus Points

◆ Counting the number of students in the class

◆ Exploring math manipulatives and their attributes

◆ Developing language to describe shapes, position, and quantity

Vocabulary

double-checking

Today's Plan		Materials
ACTIVITY **1 Introducing Counting Around the Circle**	5–10 MIN CLASS	• Materials for *Attendance* (from Session 1.1)
MATH WORKSHOP **2 Exploring Materials** **2A Exploring Pattern Blocks** **2B Exploring Geoblocks** **2C Exploring Connecting Cubes**	20–30 MIN	2A • Materials from Session 1.1, p. 24 2B • Materials from Session 1.1, p. 24 2C • Materials from Session 1.1, p. 24
DISCUSSION **3 Checking In**	5 MIN CLASS	
SESSION FOLLOW-UP **4 Homework**		• M1–M2, Family Letter*

*See *Materials to Prepare,* p. 21.

Classroom Routines

Attendance The Classroom Routine is part of the math class in this session. Students revisit the *Attendance* routine, counting the number of students in two different ways.

ACTIVITY

1 Introducing Counting Around the Circle

5–10 MIN CLASS

Count the students as you did in Session 1.1. After you have counted the number of students present and absent and the total number of students in the class, introduce counting around the circle, or counting off, as another way to count and double-check the number of students present. ❶

It's always a good idea to count things more than once. This is called double-checking. We can double-check the number of people who are here today by counting around our circle. Here's the way counting around the circle works: The first person says, "one," and the second person says, "two." What do you think the third person will say? What about the fourth person?

Designate one student as the first person. Help students learn how to count around the circle by pointing to each child when it is his or her turn to say a number. Some students will need help figuring out the next number. Encourage everyone in the group to help one another. This will begin to establish a climate in which students are comfortable asking for and giving help. ❷

The class counts around the circle.

When you have finished, fill in the information on your Attendance Recording Sheet, on the board, or on chart paper. ❸

Teaching Notes

❶ **Counting Off** It takes time for students to develop an understanding of this procedure. For some, it is not apparent that the number they say stands for the number of people counted thus far. Instead, they relate this number to a more familiar one, their age. Students may say, "But I'm not 8, I'm 5." When this happens, explain that they are counting off to find out how many students are in the circle and that the number 8 stands for all of the students who have been counted so far.

❸ **The *Attendance* Routine** Variations are provided for this Classroom Routine over the course of the year to reflect students' growing understanding of numbers and counting.

Professional Development

❷ **Dialogue Box:** *I'm Not 8, I'm 5!*, p. 139

Professional Development

4 **Teacher Note:** Exploring Materials: Introducing Math Vocabulary, p. 134

MATH WORKSHOP

2 Exploring Materials

20–30 MIN

Explain that the same three activities from the previous session are available again for this session. 4

Review your expectations about making choices, using and caring for materials, and working with others. If any issues came up yesterday, remind students of them and of the strategies they brainstormed for handling them fairly. Then help students choose an activity and get started.

Use the questions in Session 1.1, page 27 to gather information about how students make choices and involve themselves with activities.

About ten minutes before the end-of-session discussion, let students know that they have about five minutes left to work. After five minutes, ask students to clean up their materials, check the floor for stray cubes or blocks, and return all materials to their containers.

2A Exploring Pattern Blocks

INDIVIDUALS PAIRS GROUPS

For complete details about this activity, see Session 1.1, page 28.

2B Exploring Geoblocks

INDIVIDUALS PAIRS GROUPS

For complete details about this activity, see Session 1.1, pages 29–30.

2C Exploring Connecting Cubes

INDIVIDUALS PAIRS GROUPS

For complete details about this activity, see Session 1.1, pages 30–31.

DISCUSSION

3 Checking In

5 MIN CLASS

Just as you did at the end of Session 1.1, take this opportunity to discuss any logistical or management issues that arose while students worked.

As time permits, also ask students about how they are using the materials and what they are noticing about them. Keep such conversations open and brief.

What sorts of things have you been doing and making with the pattern blocks? Connecting cubes? Geoblocks?

Who can tell us something they noticed about the pattern blocks? connecting cubes? Geoblocks? Who noticed something different?

One student shares her observations about Geoblocks.

Because listening is difficult for many kindergarteners, their attention is likely to wander if every student shares. Instead, ask a student to share what he or she did, and then encourage others to think about how what they did was similar.

[Carmen] told us that she built a Geoblock castle. Raise your hand if you built a castle or another kind of building. What kind of building did you make? Who used the Geoblocks to make something that was not a building? Tell us about that.

DIFFERENTIATION: Supporting the Range of Learners

ELL To help English Language Learners follow these end-of-session conversations, you can hold up an example of each of the materials being discussed or point to pictures of these materials that you have posted in the classroom. To support English Language Learners' participation in these discussions, make sure to ask them to share their work during one of the upcoming discussions.

SESSION FOLLOW-UP

4 Homework

Family Letter: Send home copies of the Family Letter (M1–M2) with each student.

The Calendar Routine

Math Focus Points

◆ Using the calendar as a tool for keeping track of time and events

◆ Using the calendar to count days

◆ Connecting number names, numerals, and quantities

◆ Exploring math manipulatives and their attributes

Today's Plan			Materials
ACTIVITY **①** **Introducing the** *Calendar* **Routine**	🕐 10 MIN	👥 CLASS	• A pocket calendar with removable numbers; other types of calendars, such as a date book or a yearlong calendar (optional); "Today" marker*
MATH WORKSHOP **②** **Exploring Materials** **2A** **Exploring Pattern Blocks** **2B** **Exploring Geoblocks** **2C** **Exploring Connecting Cubes**	🕐 15–30 MIN		**2A** • Materials from Session 1.1, p. 24 **2B** • Materials from Session 1.1, p. 24 **2C** • Materials from Session 1.1, p. 24
DISCUSSION **③** **Checking In**	🕐 5 MIN	👥 CLASS	
SESSION FOLLOW-UP **④** **Practice**			• *Student Math Handbook Flip Chart*, p. 15

*See *Materials to Prepare*, p. 21.

Classroom Routines

Attendance: Counting Around the Circle   As in Session 1.2, students count the number of students aloud with you as you point to each child. Then, beginning with one student, they count around the circle again to double-check the count.

ACTIVITY
Introducing the *Calendar* Routine

10 MIN   CLASS

Display the class calendar so that students can easily view it while working as a whole group, ideally somewhere in your meeting area. The numbers (dates), month, and days of the week should all be in place and visible. ❶ ❷ ❸

This is a calendar. Who has an idea about what a calendar is? Where do you see calendars? What do people use them for? Have you ever seen or used a calendar? Have you ever seen someone else use one?

Encourage students to share their ideas, keeping in mind that some students have some notion of what calendars are and what they are used for, while others have had little experience with them. ❹

We are going to use this calendar all year long to help us keep track of what day it is. Right now our calendar shows that the name of this month is [September]. What do you notice about our calendar for [September]?

Students' observations usually vary widely. They notice things that do relate to the calendar as a tool for keeping track of time (the numbers) and things that do not (the color of different parts of the calendar). Accept all suggestions equally, but if students do not comment on the important features, briefly mention and discuss them.

[Abby] noticed that our calendar has letters on it. Where do you see letters?

Math Notes

❶ **The *Calendar* Routine** This activity—and the variations suggested over the course of this unit and year—helps students develop an understanding of the calendar as a tool for keeping track of time and events. It also provides a place for regular practice with counting, with written numbers, and with connecting the number names (five), numerals (5), and quantities (in this case, days). See the full write-up for this routine in **Part 4: Classroom Routines** in *Implementing Investigations in Kindergarten: Calendar.*

❷ **Patterns on the Calendar** The Kindergarten Calendar routine focuses on the structure of a calendar and on patterns inherent in it: the counting sequence of 7 days in a week and the repeating cycle of 7 days, and 12 months.

Teaching Note

❸ **Other Types of Calendars** If possible, show students several kinds of calendars. Some students relate more to wall calendars or date or appointment books. Further, seeing multiple examples expands others' ideas about what a calendar is. Consider hanging a 12-month calendar in your classroom as another example for students to use.

Professional Development

❹ **Dialogue Box:** What's a Calendar?, p. 140

Encourage students to point out where they see letters on your calendar. Briefly explain what the words are and what they mean.

A student shows what she notices about the pocket calendar.

This big word up here tells us the name of the month. This month is [September]. These other words down here are the days of the week: Sunday, Monday, Tuesday, Wednesday, Thursday, Friday, and Saturday.

In addition to the names of the month and the days of the week, be sure to discuss the numbers and what they mean.

[Raul] says the calendar has numbers on it. What do you think the numbers mean?

Some students have ideas about what the numbers on the calendar are for, while others may not recognize many (or any) of the numerals.

The numbers help us keep track of the days in a month. So the number 1 [points to 1] was the first day of [September], and the number 2 [points to 2] was the second day . . . How many days do you think there are in the whole month of September?

Encourage students to share and explain their ideas. Then, ask them to count the numbers on the calendar together with you, explaining that they need to count only as high as they can. Typically, students can count much higher when they count with the whole class than they can alone. Because students learn to count by having many opportunities to do so and by hearing others do so, count all of the days in the month, even as students drop out of the count.

Another important feature of the class calendar is the marker that shows "Today". If students have not noticed this feature, explain what it is and place it on today's date.

The calendar helps us keep track of what day it is. I made a marker so that it will be easy to see which day is today. What number is today? How can we figure this out?

Ask a volunteer to count to the number, or do this together as a class.

[Corey] counted up to [seven] today. She counted [1, 2, 3, 4, 5, 6, 7] [touch each number card]. So today is the [seventh] day of [September].

MATH WORKSHOP

15–30 MIN

2 Exploring Materials

Explain that the same three activities are available during Math Workshop today.

2A Exploring Pattern Blocks

INDIVIDUALS PAIRS GROUPS

For complete details about this activity, see Session 1.1, page 28.

2B Exploring Geoblocks

INDIVIDUALS PAIRS GROUPS

For complete details about this activity, see Session 1.1, pages 29–30.

2C Exploring Connecting Cubes

INDIVIDUALS PAIRS GROUPS

For complete details about this activity, see Session 1.1, pages 30–31.

DISCUSSION

5 MIN CLASS

3 Checking In

As you have been doing, take this opportunity to check in with students. You might talk about any logistical or management issues that arose while students worked, as described in Session 1.1, page 31. You can also discuss how students are using the materials, as described in Session 1.2, pages 34–35.

Teaching Note

⑤ Sharing Designs and Constructions Offering students opportunities to share their work and see the work of others stimulates new ideas and thinking among even the youngest students. Since students' work will not be very portable, give them several minutes at the end of the session, just before clean up, to walk around and look at work in progress. Or students can work on trays or sturdy cardboard mats and bring them to the meeting area.

As students become familiar with Math Workshop and do not need to spend as much time discussing logistical or management issues, you can use this check-in time for students to share some of their work. ⑤

Students share their pattern block designs.

SESSION FOLLOW-UP

4 Practice

Student Math Handbook Flip Chart: Use the *Student Math Handbook Flip Chart* page 15 to reinforce concepts from today's session. See pages 144–148 in the back of this unit.

Calendar: Adding Special Days

Math Focus Points

- Using the calendar as a tool for keeping track of time and events
- Connecting number names, numerals, and quantities
- Exploring math manipulatives and their attributes

Today's Plan		Materials
ACTIVITY **① Introducing Special Days on the *Calendar***	10 MIN · CLASS	• A pocket calendar with removable numbers (from Session 1.3); cards, tags or markers for highlighting special days*
MATH WORKSHOP **② Exploring Materials** **2A Exploring Pattern Blocks** **2B Exploring Geoblocks** **2C Exploring Connecting Cubes**	15–30 MIN	**2A** • Materials from Session 1.1, p. 24 **2B** • Materials from Session 1.1, p. 24 **2C** • Materials from Session 1.1, p. 24
DISCUSSION **③ Checking In**	5 MIN · CLASS	
SESSION FOLLOW-UP **④ Practice**		• *Student Math Handbook Flip Chart,* pp. 15, 16

*See *Materials to Prepare,* p. 23.

Classroom Routines

Attendance: Counting Around the Circle Students count the number of students aloud with you, as a volunteer points to each child. Then, beginning with one student, count around the circle, to double-check the count.

ACTIVITY

① Introducing Special Days on the *Calendar*

10 MIN   CLASS

As you did in Session 1.3, review what students notice about the calendar. Move the "Today" marker forward one day and count to figure out today's date. Then introduce the calendar as a tool for keeping track of special events.

Another thing people use calendars for is to keep track of when special days or events happen. There are a few special days this month that we need to remember.

Show students the cards or tags that you made to mark the special days and—based on the illustrations on the cards—ask them to predict what will happen on those days.

[Lionel] thinks that this picture of an [apple tree] means that we are going [apple picking]. [Lionel's] right! On [September 25], we are going to [an orchard to pick apples]. Where do you think I should put the picture of [the apple tree] so we all remember what day our [field trip] is?

Some students recognize the number, but most suggest counting. Note that dates under 10 are the ones that students are more likely to be able to find themselves.

[Emma] thinks this is the number 20. Let's count to check.

Count to the date as a class and then place the card on the calendar. Do the same for each special-day card. ❶

MATH WORKSHOP

Exploring Materials

15–30 MIN

Explain that the same three activities are available during Math Workshop today.

2A Exploring Pattern Blocks

INDIVIDUALS   PAIRS   GROUPS

For complete details about this activity, see Session 1.1, page 28.

2B Exploring Geoblocks

INDIVIDUALS   PAIRS   GROUPS

For complete details about this activity, see Session 1.1, pages 29–30.

2C Exploring Connecting Cubes

INDIVIDUALS   PAIRS   GROUPS

For complete details about this activity, see Session 1.1, pages 30–31.

DISCUSSION

Checking In

5 MIN   CLASS

As you have been doing, take this opportunity to check in with students. You might talk about any logistical or management issues that arose as described in Session 1.1, page 31. You can also discuss how students are using the materials, as described in Session 1.2, pages 34–35; or have more students share their work, as suggested in Session 1.3, pages 39–40.

SESSION FOLLOW-UP

Practice

 Student Math Handbook Flip Chart: Use the *Student Math Handbook Flip Chart* pages 15, 16 to reinforce concepts from today's session. See pages 144–148 in the back of this unit.

Comparing Materials

Math Focus Points

◆ Exploring math manipulatives and their attributes

Today's Plan		Materials
MATH WORKSHOP **① Exploring Materials** **1A Exploring Pattern Blocks** **1B Exploring Geoblocks** **1C Exploring Connecting Cubes**	20–35 MIN	**1A** • Materials from Session 1.1, p. 24 **1B** • Materials from Session 1.1, p. 24 **1C** • Materials from Session 1.1, p. 24
DISCUSSION **② Comparing Materials**	10 MIN CLASS	• Pattern blocks; Geoblocks; connecting cubes
SESSION FOLLOW-UP **③ Practice**		• *Student Activity Book*, p. 1

Classroom Routines

Calendar Review the name of the month, the days of the week, and any upcoming special events. Have students help you place the "Today" marker and count to the number that is today's date.

MATH WORKSHOP

1 Exploring Materials

20–35 MIN

Explain to students that the same three activities are available during Math Workshop today, but that tomorrow the materials they are exploring will change.

1A Exploring Pattern Blocks

INDIVIDUALS   PAIRS   GROUPS

For complete details about this activity, see Sessions 1.1, page 28.

1B Exploring Geoblocks

INDIVIDUALS   PAIRS   GROUPS

For complete details about this activity, see Session 1.1, pages 29–30.

Students explore Geoblocks.

1C Exploring Connecting Cubes

INDIVIDUALS   PAIRS   GROUPS

For complete details about this activity, see Session 1.1, pages 30–31.

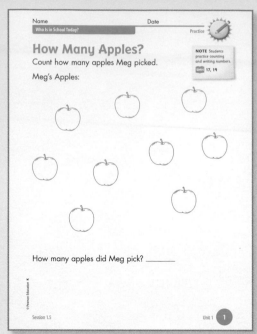

Name _____ Date _____

Who Is in School Today?   Practice

How Many Apples?

Count how many apples Meg picked.

Meg's Apples:

> NOTE Students
> practice counting
> and writing numbers.
> SMH 17, 19

How many apples did Meg pick? _____

Session 1.5   Unit 1 ①

▲ **Student Activity Book, p. 1**

10 MIN   CLASS

② Comparing Materials

Math Focus Points for Discussion

◆ Exploring math manipulatives and their attributes

By this session, most or all students should have had the opportunity to explore each of the materials available during Math Workshop. Now you can have students compare the materials by asking them some of the following questions.

- How are the pattern blocks and the Geoblocks the same? How are they different?

- How are the pattern blocks and connecting cubes the same? How are they different?

- Are there things you could do with the cubes that you couldn't do with the pattern blocks or Geoblocks?

- How did you use the pattern blocks and the Geoblocks differently?

If there are logistical or management-related issues that you need to address, discuss those as well.

SESSION FOLLOW-UP

③ Practice

 Practice: For reinforcement of this unit's content, have students complete *Student Activity Book* page 1.

Making an Attendance Stick

Math Focus Points

◆ Counting the number of students in the class

◆ Establishing one-to-one correspondence between equal groups (e.g., students and cubes)

◆ Exploring math manipulatives and their attributes

◆ Developing language to describe shapes, position, and quantity

Today's Plan		Materials
ACTIVITY **① Introducing the Attendance Stick**	10 MIN CLASS	• Materials for *Attendance* (from Session 1.1) • Connecting cubes*
ACTIVITY **② Introducing More Math Materials**	5 MIN CLASS	• Color tiles*; buttons*; attribute blocks*; tray or sturdy cardboard work mat
MATH WORKSHOP **③ Exploring More Materials** **3A Exploring Color Tiles** **3B Exploring Attribute Blocks** **3C Exploring Buttons**	10–25 MIN	**3A** • Color tiles*; tray or sturdy cardboard work mat (optional) **3B** • Attribute blocks*; tray or sturdy cardboard work mat (optional) **3C** • Buttons*; tray or sturdy cardboard work mat (optional)
DISCUSSION **④ Checking In**	5 MIN CLASS	
SESSION FOLLOW-UP **⑤ Practice**		• *Student Math Handbook Flip Chart,* pp. 17, 18

*See *Materials to Prepare*, p. 23.

Classroom Routines

Calendar Review the name of the month, the days of the week, and any upcoming special events. Have students help you place the "Today" marker, and count to the number that is today's date.

ACTIVITY

Introducing the Attendance Stick

10 MIN   CLASS

As in previous sessions, establish the number of students present by counting them in two different ways.

- Count as a group as you and/or students point to each child.

- Count around the circle with each student saying one number.

Establish who is absent and then record the information on the Attendance Recording Sheet, the board, or chart paper.

Every day we take attendance; we count the number of students who are here in two different ways. Now we're going to add on to this.

Pass the bin of one-color connecting cubes around the circle and have each student take one.

Students each take a connecting cube that they will use to build an Attendance Stick.

We just figured out that there are [24] students here today, and that [Raul] is absent. Everyone just took one cube. If I collect all of the cubes and snap them together, how many cubes do you think we will have?

Some students will recognize that the number of cubes should be the same as the total number of students in the class, but many will not see this connection yet. As students offer their ideas, encourage them to explain their thinking.

Collect the cubes one-by-one, snapping them together into a tower. Encourage students to count the cubes with you as you add them to the tower.

Our cube tower has [24] cubes in it because there are [24] students in our class today. But [Raul] is not here today, so he did not take a cube. We need to add one cube to our tower for [Raul] How many cubes will be in our tower if we add [Raul's] cube?

Although some students will be able to say how many cubes are in the tower, numbers in the 20s may be large and unfamiliar to many. Verify the total number of cubes in the tower by having students count the cubes as you hold and touch each cube as they count with you.

This cube tower is very special because it has one cube for every student in our class when everyone is here. It shows how many people are in our class. That's why I call it our Class Stick or Attendance Stick. Each day, when we count the number of people who are in school, we can use it to talk about the number of people who are here, and the number of people who are not here.

Find a visible and easily accessible place to display the Attendance Stick. It will be used throughout the year during the *Attendance* routine.

ACTIVITY

2 Introducing More Math Materials

5 MIN   CLASS

Show students a bucket of color tiles, a bin of buttons, one subset of attribute blocks, and—if students are to use them—a tray or cardboard mat. Then briefly introduce these materials.

During this Math Workshop, students explore attribute blocks, color tiles, and buttons.

Teaching Notes

❷ Color Tiles Color tiles come in four colors: red, yellow, blue, and green. In *Investigations,* students use color tiles to explore patterns and counting and to think about arrangements and combinations of different numbers.

❸ Dominoes Students quickly discover that tiles can be set up (and toppled over) like dominoes. Allow students to use the tiles in whatever way they choose, as long as they are within the limits of responsible play. Later in the year when you ask students to use tiles for a specific task, they'll be less tempted to play with them. Some teachers set up a special area for these domino structures where the entire class can gather for the topple-over. In these classrooms, the novelty and excitement soon wears off and students move on to using the tiles in other ways.

These are a few more of the tools we will use to solve math problems and to play math games this year. Do any of these materials look familiar? Have you used any of them before?

Just as with connecting cubes, pattern blocks, and Geoblocks, you will have time to freely explore these materials over the next week.

Show students where the materials are stored and be sure to discuss how students should use, share, and care for them. Also, let students know how many children each activity can accommodate.

MATH WORKSHOP

10–25 MIN

③ Exploring More Materials

Help students choose among the following three activities.

③A Exploring Color Tiles

INDIVIDUALS   PAIRS   GROUPS

Students explore a set of 1-inch square tiles in four colors. They are useful for pattern-making, sorting, counting, and other number-related activities.❷

ONGOING ASSESSMENT: Observing Students at Work

Students explore color tiles and their attributes.

- **How do students use the tiles?** Do they lay them flat? Stand them on edge? Stack them? What do they make with them (e.g., pictures, designs, towers, patterns, rectangles, and dominoes)?❸

Students explore color tiles.

- **How do students describe the tiles and creations?** Do they refer to them by shape? By color? Do they have language to describe the position of different tiles (e.g., above/below, in front of/behind, next to, near)?

3B Exploring Attribute Blocks

INDIVIDUALS   PAIRS   GROUPS

Students explore attribute blocks—a set of flat blocks that share similar features. They vary in shape (hexagon, square, rectangle, and circle), color (red, yellow, blue), size (small and large) and thickness (thick and thin).

ONGOING ASSESSMENT: Observing Students at Work

Students explore the attribute blocks.

- **How do students use the attribute blocks?** Do they sort them? Make pictures or designs? Stack them?

- **How do they describe individual blocks?** Do they refer to them by color? Size? Shape? Thickness? What words do they use?

- **Do students have language to describe the position of different blocks in relation to one another (e.g., above/below, in front of/behind, next to, near)?**

3C Exploring Buttons

INDIVIDUALS   PAIRS   GROUPS

Students explore buttons—a material that is useful for counting, sorting, and pattern-making activities.

ONGOING ASSESSMENT: Observing Students at Work

Students explore buttons.

- **What do students do with the buttons?** Do they sort them? Count them? Make patterns or designs with them?

- **What attributes do students notice (e.g., size, color, number of holes, type of material)?** What words do they use to describe such attributes?

Teaching Notes

④ **Attribute Blocks** Each attribute block can be described by size, color, shape, and thickness (e.g., a small, thin, yellow square). Each block can be compared with others by determining similarities and differences among these attributes. For example, the small, yellow square is similar to the small, red circle because they are both small. However, it is different from the large, blue triangle in three ways. Unlike the other materials in this unit, attribute blocks must stay as a discrete set. Help students recognize the number of pieces in each set and remind them to keep the attribute blocks together.

⑤ **Buttons** Students may count or make designs with the buttons, but they are most likely to sort them. Unlike the attribute blocks that have a limited number of attributes to sort by, buttons have many. In fact, the variety of attributes may at first be somewhat overwhelming for kindergarteners. They may group buttons only by color or match the ones that are exactly the same. With experience, students may begin to pay attention to less obvious attributes, such as the number of holes, while disregarding more obvious attributes, such as color.

DISCUSSION

Checking In

5 MIN   CLASS

As you have at the end of each session in this Investigation, take this opportunity to discuss any logistical or management issues that arose while students worked. Topics might include the following:

- The number of students each activity can accommodate

- Using and sharing materials

- Caring for and storing materials

- Noise level

- Making choices

- Working with a partner or group

- Working purposefully

For example, you might act out a scenario—such as handling materials roughly or choosing one activity, quickly choosing another, and then wandering to another—and ask students to comment on what they notice. Then you can explain and discuss your expectations of students during Math Workshop and the reasoning behind them.

As time permits, also ask students about how they are using the materials and what they are noticing about them. Keep such conversations open and brief.

SESSION FOLLOW-UP

Practice

 Student Math Handbook Flip Chart: Use the *Student Math Handbook Flip Chart* pages 17, 18 to reinforce concepts from today's session. See pages 144–148 in the back of this unit.

Mathematical Emphases

Counting and Quantity Developing strategies for accurately counting a set of objects by 1s

Math Focus Points

◆ Developing strategies for accurately counting and keeping track of quantities up to 10

◆ Creating an equivalent set

◆ Establishing one-to-one correspondence between equal groups (e.g., students and cubes)

◆ Developing strategies for accurately counting and keeping track of quantities up to the number of students in the class

Data Analysis Sorting and Classifying

Math Focus Points

◆ Identifying attributes (e.g., color, size, and shape) and developing language to describe them

◆ Comparing how objects are the same and different

◆ Finding objects that share one attribute

Whole Number Operations Using manipulatives, drawings, tools, and notation to show strategies and solutions

Math Focus Points

◆ Exploring math manipulatives and their attributes

The Counting Jar

	Student Activity Book	Student Math Handbook Flip Chart	Professional Development: Read Ahead of Time	
SESSION 2.1 p. 58				
The Counting Jar Students are introduced to the Counting Jar, an activity that asks them to count the objects in a jar and then create an equivalent set. During Math Workshop, students work with the Counting Jar and continue to explore math materials.		20	• **Teacher Note:** Counting Is More Than 1, 2, 3, p. 127; Observing Kindergarteners as They Count, p. 135	
SESSION 2.2 p. 64				
Describing Buttons Students revisit the *Attendance* routine, using the cube tower created at the end of Investigation 1. During Math Workshop, students explore materials and continue to visit the Counting Jar. Class discussion focuses on describing buttons.		20, 47		
SESSION 2.3 p. 70				
Button Match-Up Students are introduced to *Button Match-Up,* a game that asks them to find buttons that match by at least one attribute. Math Workshop focuses on exploring materials and their attributes and on counting.	2		• **Teacher Note:** Sorting and Identifying Attributes, p. 136	

Classroom Routines See page 16 for an overview.

Calendar	*Attendance*
• Pocket calendar	• Name tags for each student
• "Today" marker	• Attendance Recording Sheet
	• Attendance Stick

Materials to Gather	Materials to Prepare
• **Materials for Exploring Color Tiles** See Session 1.6, p. 47. • **Materials for Exploring Attribute Blocks** See Session 1.6, p. 47. • **Materials for Exploring Buttons** See Session 1.6, p. 47. • **Literature selection about counting** See Family Letter, M4, for suggestions. (optional)	• **M5, Assessment Checklist: Counting** ☑ (3–4 per class, plus extras as needed) • **Counting Jar** Obtain a clear plastic jar or container that is at least 6 inches tall. The mouth of the jar should be at least 4–5 inches in diameter. For Activity 1, put 7 cubes in the jar. For Math Workshop, place 4 counters (e.g., teddy bear counters) in the jar. • **Resealable plastic bags, or paper plates** Label with students' names. (1 per student)
• **Materials for *Attendance*** See Session 1.1, p. 21. • **Attendance Stick** (from Session 1.6) • **Materials for Counting Jar** See Session 2.1. • **Materials for Exploring Color Tiles** See Session 1.6, p. 47. • **Materials for Exploring Attribute Blocks** See Session 1.6, p. 47. • **Materials for Exploring Buttons** See Session 1.6, p. 47.	• **Chart paper** Title a piece of chart paper, "Describing a Button."
• **Chart: "Describing a Button"** See Session 2.2. • **Buttons** (1 handful per pair) • **Tray or sturdy cardboard work mat** (1 per student; optional) • **Materials for Counting Jar** See Session 2.1. • **Materials for Exploring Color Tiles** See Session 1.6, p. 47. • **Materials for Exploring Attribute Blocks** See Session 1.6, p. 47.	

☑ Checklist Available

The Counting Jar, *continued*

	Student Activity Book	Student Math Handbook Flip Chart	Professional Development: Read Ahead of Time	
SESSION 2.4 p. 76				
Attribute Block Match-Up Students are introduced to *Attribute Block Match-Up,* a game that asks them to find attribute blocks that share at least one attribute. Math Workshop focuses on exploring materials and their attributes and on counting.		47		
SESSION 2.5 p. 82				
Counting Jar: How Many Did You Find? Students are introduced to the final aspect of the *Attendance* routine, an Attendance Stick with number labels. Math Workshop focuses on exploring materials and their attributes and on counting. Class discussion focuses on how students figured out how many objects were in the Counting Jar and how they created an equivalent set.	3			

Materials to Gather	Materials to Prepare
• **Materials for** *Button Match-Up* See Session 2.3. • **Materials for Counting Jar** See Session 2.1. • **Materials for Exploring Color Tiles** See Session 1.6, p. 47.	• **Attribute blocks** Divide each of the two sets in half if you want four pairs to do this activity instead of two pairs. Put all of the thin blocks in one group and all the thick blocks in another group.
• **Materials for** *Attribute Block Match-Up* See Session 2.4. • **Materials for** *Button Match-Up* See Session 2.3. • **Materials for Counting Jar** See Session 2.1. • **Materials for Exploring Color Tiles** See Session 1.6, p. 47. • **Bin of other counters, such as cubes or tiles**	• **Labeled Attendance Stick** Make a cube tower with as many cubes as there are students in your class. Write the numbers 1 through the total number of students in your class on stick-on dots and place one on each cube. • **Counting Jar** Place 4 teddy bears counters in the jar. • **M3–M4, Family Letter** Make copies. (1 per student)

The Counting Jar

Math Focus Points

◆ Developing strategies for accurately counting and keeping track of quantities up to 10

◆ Creating an equivalent set

◆ Exploring math manipulatives and their attributes

Today's Plan		Materials
ACTIVITY **❶ Introducing the Counting Jar**	10 MIN CLASS	• Counting Jar*; bins of various types of counters*; resealable plastic bags or paper plates*; literature selection about counting (optional)
MATH WORKSHOP **❷ Counting and Exploring Materials** ② Counting Jar ② Exploring Color Tiles ② Exploring Attribute Blocks ② Exploring Buttons	15–30 MIN	② • M5 ☑ * • Counting Jar*; various types of counters; resealable plastic bags or paper plates* ② • Materials from Session 1.6, p. 47 ② • Materials from Session 1.6, p. 47 ② • Materials from Session 1.6, p. 47
DISCUSSION **❸ Checking In**	5 MIN CLASS	
SESSION FOLLOW-UP **❹ Practice**		• *Student Math Handbook Flip Chart*, p. 20

*See *Materials to Prepare*, p. 55.

Classroom Routines

Calendar Review the name of the month, the days of the week, and any upcoming special events. Have students help you place the "Today" marker, and count to the number that is today's date.

ACTIVITY
1 Introducing the Counting Jar

10 MIN CLASS

Consider beginning this activity with a story that relates to the mathematical focus at hand—counting. For example, *Mouse Count*, by Ellen Stoll Walsh, counts and "uncounts" a group of mice as they are put into and escape from a jar. Other alternatives are listed in the Family Letter (M3–M4). Then, gather students around the table where you have placed the Counting Jar.

We have been doing a lot of counting; we count the number of students who are in school each day, and we count on the calendar to find out what day it is. We are going to do a lot of counting this year.

Show students the Counting Jar with seven cubes inside it.❶ ❷

This is a special kind of jar called a Counting Jar. We'll be using it all year long. What do you notice about the Counting Jar? [Manuel] says there are cubes in there. How could we find out how many cubes are in the jar?

Some students will try to count the cubes within the jar. Others will suggest taking the cubes out of the jar to count them. Ask several volunteers to demonstrate how they would count the objects. Ask other students to watch closely to see what they notice about how each person counts.

*[Rebecca] is going to show us how she would count the cubes. Watch to see how she counts. What do you notice about how Rebecca counted the cubes?*❸

A student counts the objects in the Counting Jar as her classmates look on.

Teaching Notes

❶ **Counting Jar** Students will do this activity, and the recording piece introduced in Session 3.2, in every unit of the *Investigations* sequence. Once established, some teachers make the Counting Jar available to students outside of math time—as they enter the classroom in the morning or during any free times.

❷ **The Math of the Counting Jar** Many primary classrooms have an estimation jar. However, estimating requires an understanding of the quantities involved. The Counting Jar focuses on helping young students develop that understanding by giving them repeated practice with counting sets of objects, creating sets of a given size, and recording quantitative information.

❸ **Handling Mistakes** Kindergarteners' counting experience can vary widely; expect to see mistakes. How you handle them (modeling how to give helpful feedback or treating mistakes as an opportunity for everyone to learn) is an important part of developing a mathematical community in which students feel safe, are comfortable sharing ideas, and are able to take risks and make mistakes. Focus on the challenges of and strategies for counting accurately and on the importance of double-checking. Students learn how to count fluently by having many opportunities to count and by watching others count.

Teaching Note

❹ Creating an Equivalent Set This step provides additional counting practice but also presents a different type of task. For some students, counting a given set (e.g., "Here are some cubes. Can you count them?") is quite different from creating a set of a given size. ("Can you count out seven cubes for me?") Display the sets of objects so that everyone can see them.

Professional Development

❺ Teacher Note: Counting Is More Than 1, 2, 3, p. 127

❻ Teacher Note: Observing Kindergarteners as They Count, p. 135

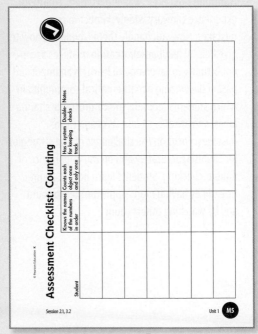

Assessment Checklist: Counting

Session 2.1, 3.2   Unit 1 **M5**

▲ **Resource Masters, M5** ✓

After several students have counted the cubes, count them together as a class.

We counted seven cubes in the Counting Jar. Now we're going to make another collection of seven things to match the number we found in the jar.

Show students the bins of different counters. Ask several volunteers to count out seven objects from each bin into a resealable plastic bag (or onto a paper plate or other container). Ask different volunteers to double-check the amount in each collection.❹

Now we have lots of different groups of seven objects. There are seven cubes in the Counting Jar, and now we have sets of seven [buttons, tiles, and pennies].

Explain that students will visit the Counting Jar during Math Workshop and that it is an activity they will return to throughout the school year.

Before Math Workshop, I'm going to put a different set of objects in the Counting Jar. When you visit the Counting Jar, your job is to find out how many things are in it. After you count the objects, you need to make another set with the same number as the jar. So, if the Counting Jar has six [bears] in it, you need to make a group of six [pennies] or [cubes] or [keys] in the plastic bag [or on the paper plate] that has your name on it.

MATH WORKSHOP

15–30 MIN

❷ Counting and Exploring Materials

Explain that the following activities are available during Math Workshop. Remind students what each activity entails, what materials are required, and where they are located. Spend most of your time helping students with the Counting Jar and observing them as they count and create an equivalent set.

❷ⓐ Counting Jar
INDIVIDUALS

Students count the number of objects in the Counting Jar and create an equivalent set. By observing them, you can develop an initial sense of their familiarity and comfort with the counting sequence and the process of counting. Use Assessment Checklist: Counting (M5) to keep track of your observations about their skills over the course of this unit.❺ ❻

Assessment Checklist: Counting

Student	Knows the names of the numbers in order	Counts each object once and only once	Has a system for keeping track	Double-checks	Notes
Jennifer	✓ yes 1–4	yes—touches each bear	yes	yes—recounts as she puts bears back in jar	dumps bears out to count
Manuel	✓ yes 1–4	immediately says 4 w/out counting			When I asked how he knew w/out counting, he said, "I can see 4. I counted with my eyes."
Mia	✓ yes 1–4	counts slowly and purposefully	yes—moves each bear aside		
Yoshio	✓ yes but miscounts and gets 5 not 4	no—double counts and gets 5	not really	no	

ONGOING ASSESSMENT: Observing Students at Work

Students count a set of objects and create a set of the same size. As they compare two sets, they encounter another situation that illustrates one-to-one correspondence.

- **How familiar are students with the sequence of number names?** Do they omit, repeat, or mix the order of some numbers? Which ones?

- **How do students count the objects in the jar?** Do they remove them and count one object at a time? Do they empty the jar and count the objects as they put them back in? Do they dump the jar and then count the objects? Do they organize the objects in some way? Do they touch or move each item as they count it? Do any students double-check their count?

- **How do students create an equivalent set?** Do they count out the amount? (e.g., "There were four teddy bears, so I need four cubes.") Do they take one [cube] for each [teddy bear]? (Note: Students who use this strategy can create an equivalent set *without* counting.) Once finished, do students compare their set to the set in the jar? How do they decide whether the sets are the same?

DIFFERENTIATION: Supporting the Range of Learners

Intervention Students learn the number sequence and counting by having repeated chances to count and to watch others count. Encourage students who do not yet have a solid grasp of the number sequence to count again from the beginning, to count on from where you leave off (or to correct your count), to count with you, or to repeat the numbers after you as you count.

Intervention Suggest that students who have difficulty making an equivalent set, match one counter to each object in the jar.

2B Exploring Color Tiles

INDIVIDUALS   PAIRS   GROUPS

For complete details about this activity, see Session 1.6, page 50.

2C Exploring Attribute Blocks

INDIVIDUALS   PAIRS   GROUPS

For complete details about this activity, see Session 1.6, page 51.

2D Exploring Buttons

INDIVIDUALS   PAIRS   GROUPS

For complete details about this activity, see Session 1.6, page 51.

DISCUSSION
Checking In

5 MIN CLASS

As you have throughout the unit, take this opportunity to talk about any logistical or management issues and to discuss how students are using the materials and what they are noticing about them.

What sorts of things have you been doing and making with the attribute blocks? Color tiles? Buttons?

Who can tell us something you noticed about the attribute blocks? Color tiles? Buttons? Who noticed something different?

 SESSION FOLLOW-UP
Practice

 Student Math Handbook Flip Chart: Use the *Student Math Handbook Flip Chart* page 20 to reinforce concepts from today's session. See pages 144–148 in the back of this unit.

Describing Buttons

Math Focus Points

◆ Developing strategies for accurately counting and keeping track of quantities up to the number of students in the class

◆ Establishing one-to-one correspondence between equal groups (e.g., students and cubes)

◆ Identifying attributes (e.g., color, size, and shape) and developing language to describe them

Today's Plan		Materials
ACTIVITY **① Using the Attendance Stick**	5–10 MIN CLASS	• Materials for *Attendance* (from Session 1.1) • Attendance Stick (from Session 1.6)
MATH WORKSHOP **② Counting and Exploring Materials** **②A Counting Jar** **②B Exploring Color Tiles** **②C Exploring Attribute Blocks** **②D Exploring Buttons**	15–25 MIN	②A • Materials from Session 2.1, p. 58 ②B • Materials from Session 1.6, p. 47 ②C • Materials from Session 1.6, p. 47 ②D • Materials from Session 1.6, p. 47
DISCUSSION **③ Describing Buttons**	10 MIN CLASS	• Buttons; chart: "Describing a Button"*
SESSION FOLLOW-UP **④ Practice**		• *Student Math Handbook Flip Chart,* pp. 20, 47

*See *Materials to Prepare,* p. 55.

Classroom Routines

Calendar Review the name of the month, the days of the week, and any upcoming special events. Have students help you place the "Today" marker, and count to the number that is today's date.

ACTIVITY

1 Using the Attendance Stick

5–10 MIN CLASS

As in previous sessions, establish the number of students present by:

- Counting as a group as you and/or students point to each child

- Counting around the circle with each student saying one number

Establish who is absent and then fill in the Attendance Recording Sheet or record the information on the board or on chart paper. Then, ask students to consider the Attendance Stick that you made in Session 1.6 to represent the class when everyone is present.

Let's look at our Class Stick, or Attendance Stick. Who remembers what this shows? Right, it shows the number of students in our class when everyone is here. How many students are there when everyone is here?

Refer students to the information on the Attendance Recording Sheet and then count the cubes in the Attendance Stick together.

The teacher leads the class in counting the connecting cubes in the Attendance Stick.

There are [25] students in our class. When we counted around the circle today, we found out that there are [23] students in school today. I am going to break apart our Attendance Stick and see what happens when I give each of you one cube.

Give each student one of the cubes from your tower.

I gave each of you one cube. But look, we have [2] cubes left over. Why do you think that is?

Encourage students to share their ideas and then summarize.

[Carmen] and [Jason] are not here today, so these [2] cubes are the ones for [Carmen] and [Jason.] If we snap these [2] cubes together, we have a tower that shows the number of people who are absent today.

If everyone is present, use this conversation to reinforce the idea that there is one cube for every student.

Because everyone is here, when you break the stick apart, everyone gets one cube, and there are none leftover.

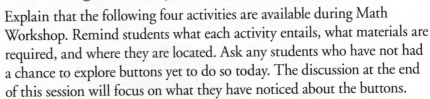

MATH WORKSHOP

15–25 MIN

② Counting and Exploring Materials

Explain that the following four activities are available during Math Workshop. Remind students what each activity entails, what materials are required, and where they are located. Ask any students who have not had a chance to explore buttons yet to do so today. The discussion at the end of this session will focus on what they have noticed about the buttons.

Continue to spend the bulk of your time at the Counting Jar, supporting students as they visit it for the first time and observing to get sense of students' familiarity and comfort with the counting sequence and the process of counting.

②A Counting Jar

INDIVIDUALS

For complete details about this activity, see Session 2.1, pages 59–60.

②B Exploring Color Tiles

INDIVIDUALS PAIRS GROUPS

For complete details about this activity, see Session 1.6, page 50.

2C Exploring Attribute Blocks

INDIVIDUALS PAIRS GROUPS

For complete details about this activity, see Session 1.6, page 51.

A student works with attribute blocks.

2D Exploring Buttons

INDIVIDUALS PAIRS GROUPS

For complete details about this activity, see Session 1.6, page 51.

DISCUSSION

3 Describing Buttons

10 MIN CLASS

Math Focus Points for Discussion

◆ Identifying attributes (e.g., color, size, and shape) and developing language to describe them

Gather students to discuss some of the things they have noticed about buttons.

Over the last few days, you have had a chance to explore a set of buttons. What did you notice about the buttons? Who noticed something different?

After students have had a chance to share, choose one button. Show it to students, perhaps passing it around so that everyone can look closely at it for a moment. If you choose a button that has duplicates in the set, you can pass around several.

Look carefully at my button. What can you tell me about it? How would you describe it? What could you say about this button so that people who can't see it could imagine what it looks like?

Label a piece of chart paper, "Describing a Button," and make a list of all the words students use to describe the button, perhaps illustrating each with a simple picture.

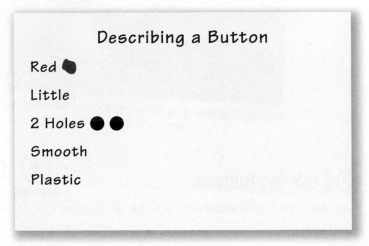

Some students will notice the color, while others will comment on its size, shape, material, texture, or its number of holes. If they have trouble describing it, ask them about specific attributes.

- What color is the button?

- Is the button shiny?

- What shape is the button?

- How many holes does the button have?

- Is the button smooth?

- What is the button made of?

When you have a good list, ask students to close their eyes and try to picture the button while you read the words aloud. If students think of other descriptive words, add them to the list. Then, tape the button to the chart. You will use the chart again in Session 2.3.

As time permits, follow the same process for another button or two. End the discussion by summarizing the sorts of things that students noticed.

*We looked really carefully at several buttons, and you noticed some really important things about buttons.*❶

You said that most of our buttons are the same shape; they are circles. We noticed that buttons can be different colors; these are black, brown, and white. We found out that buttons can be made of different things; two are plastic and one is wood. [Mia] said that they are different sizes and that this one is smaller than these two. And we talked about the holes and how there can be different numbers of holes in a button.

SESSION FOLLOW-UP
4 Practice

Student Math Handbook Flip Chart: Use the *Student Math Handbook Flip Chart* pages 20, 47 to reinforce concepts from today's session. See pages 144–148 in the back of this unit.

Teaching Note

❶ **Describing Buttons** Having opportunities to look carefully at buttons and describe their characteristics helps students begin to identify attributes and find buttons that have attributes in common. They will be doing this in Session 2.3 and beyond.

Button Match-Up

Math Focus Points

◆ Identifying attributes (e.g., color, size, and shape) and developing language to describe them

◆ Comparing how objects are the same and different

◆ Finding objects that share one attribute

Today's Plan		Materials
ACTIVITY ① **Introducing** *Button Match-Up* — 10 MIN / CLASS		• Buttons; chart: "Describing a Button" (from Session 2.2)
MATH WORKSHOP ② **Counting, Matching Attributes, and Exploring Materials** — 15–30 MIN ②A *Button Match-Up* ②B Counting Jar ②C Exploring Color Tiles ②D Exploring Attribute Blocks		②A • Buttons; trays or sturdy cardboard mats ②B • Materials from Session 2.1, p. 58 ②C • Materials from Session 1.6, p. 47 ②D • Materials from Session 1.6, p. 47
DISCUSSION ③ **Checking In** — 5 MIN / CLASS		
SESSION FOLLOW-UP ④ **Practice**		• *Student Activity Book*, p. 2

Classroom Routines

Attendance: Breaking Up the Attendance Stick Follow the regular *Attendance* routine, counting the number of students in two ways. Then, as in Session 2.2, ask students to predict what will happen if you give each student one cube from the Attendance Stick. Discuss the number of leftover cubes. (If everyone is present, use this conversation to reinforce the idea that there is one cube for every student.)

ACTIVITY

Introducing *Button Match-Up*

10 MIN   **CLASS**

Demonstrate how to take a small handful of buttons. Spread the buttons out so that students can see them.

Display the chart about buttons from Session 2.2. Untape the button and hold it up.

Yesterday, we found lots of ways to describe this button.

Encourage students to share what they remember, read their descriptions aloud, and then choose one attribute to focus on.❶

One of the ways you described this button was by its color. This button is [red]. Are there any other buttons here that are [red]?

As students find other [red] buttons, hold them next to the original button for comparison.

During Math Workshop today, you can play a game called Button Match-Up. In this game, you look for buttons that match.❷ Buttons match if there is one thing that is the same about them. These two buttons match because they are both [red]. Does anyone see another button that would match—another button that is [red]?

Follow the same process with another button or two. Hold up a new button or pass it—or several examples of it—around the circle.

Here is another button. What is one thing you notice about this button?

If students identify the same attribute, ask them to think about another.

Yes, this button is [black]. Is there anything else you notice about it? [Brad] said it has two holes. Do any of the buttons in this collection have two holes?

Professional Development

❶ **Teacher Note:** Sorting and Identifying Attributes, p. 136

Teaching Note

❷ **These Do Not Match** It can be difficult for young children to focus on one attribute rather than the whole object. For example, one student may say two buttons match because they both have two holes; another may say they do not match because one is red (and/or small) and the other is blue (and/or big). These students may think buttons match only if they are exactly the same. This is a good starting point for paying attention to attributes. As they match and sort in this unit, and in Unit 3: *What Comes Next?*, and Unit 7: *Sorting and Surveys*, students will begin to see other ways to match and sort objects.

Teaching Notes

❸ **Assigning Partners** Some teachers assign partners randomly or allow students to choose their own. Others pair children so that students who are thinking similarly (or differently) work together. Using a range of strategies helps teachers pursue mathematical goals and ensures that students learn to work with their peers, make their own choices on occasion, and learn to make good decisions.

❹ **Playing with a Partner** This is the first time students have been explicitly asked to work with a partner. Working in pairs can be challenging for young students. Be sure to make your expectations clear, perhaps role-playing common partner problems, and asking students to suggest strategies for handling them. Some teachers also model ways to be a kind, helpful, and respectful partner.

Hold up buttons that share the attribute to illustrate what you mean by a match.

These two buttons match because they both have two holes.

These two buttons match because they both have two holes.

Finally, hold up one more button.

Look closely at my button. Can you find a match? Remember, in this game, buttons match if they have at least one thing that is the same about them.

Some students choose an exact match. Others find a button that has one or two attributes that are the same. Discuss each button that is suggested, encouraging students to explain how the two buttons are the same.

Explain that during Math Workshop students will play *Button Match-Up* in pairs.❸ ❹

You and your partner need a cupful of buttons to play *Button Match-Up*. Take turns picking out a button, and then work together to find buttons that match that button.

Ask a student to play a few rounds with you to demonstrate how to play the game and how to take turns.

MATH WORKSHOP

Counting, Matching Attributes, and Exploring Materials

15–30 MIN

Explain that the following four activities are available during Math Workshop. Remind students what each activity entails, what materials are required, and where they are located.

2A *Button Match-Up*

PAIRS

Pairs try to find buttons that have at least one attribute in common.

ONGOING ASSESSMENT: Observing Students at Work

Students identify attributes and find objects that share at least one attribute.

- **Are students able to find buttons that share an attribute?** Can they explain how their buttons are the same? What language do they use?

- **Do students focus exclusively on one attribute (e.g., color) or do they match buttons according to various attributes (e.g., size, shape, color, number of holes, type of material)?**

Students play Button Match-Up.

DIFFERENTIATION: Supporting the Range of Learners

Intervention Some students match only buttons that are exactly the same. This is a good starting point for comparing attributes. Encourage these students to describe what is the same about the buttons and to look for matches that are not exactly the same. Ask questions, such as:

- How do these buttons match?

- Can you find another button that has four holes but is not big like this one?

- These buttons match—even though one is big and one is small—because they both have four holes.

ELL You may want to preview this activity with English Language Learners in a small group to be sure they understand how to play and to introduce the word *match* as it is used in this context. Place a pile of buttons in the middle of the table and sort them by a simple attribute, such as color. Select one red button and think aloud as you look for its match. I have one *red* button. Let me see if I can find *another* red button. Here is another red button. These buttons *match* because they are both the same color—red. Then place one blue button in the middle of the table. This button is *blue*. Ricardo, can you find *another* blue button? Right. These buttons *match* because they are both blue. Repeat the activity using other attributes, such as size or shape. While some English Language Learners may not yet be able to express themselves clearly in English, they can demonstrate their understanding by making several successful matches.

2B Counting Jar

INDIVIDUALS

For complete details about this activity, see Session 2.1, pages 59–60.

2C Exploring Color Tiles

INDIVIDUALS PAIRS GROUPS

For complete details about this activity, see Session 1.6, page 50.

2D Exploring Attribute Blocks

INDIVIDUALS PAIRS GROUPS

For complete details about this activity, see Session 1.6, page 51.

③ DISCUSSION
Checking In

5 MIN   CLASS

Take this opportunity to discuss any issues that you noticed while observing students at work. Because this is the first time students have been formally asked to work in pairs, you might spend this time talking about what it is like to work with a partner.

For example, describe or act out a situation in which one partner dominated play or in which a pair:

- Argued over who got to go first

- Had difficulty taking turns

- Did not talk to each other respectfully

- Could not agree on whether two buttons matched or not

Ask students to comment on what they see and to brainstorm ways to handle such a situation respectfully. Encourage students to support and listen to their partners and to solve mathematical disagreements by explaining their reasoning to each other and thinking about whether that reasoning makes sense.

If students worked well in pairs, you might decide to have a different discussion. The topic might be mathematical in nature, such as a strategy you would like all students to consider (e.g., finding a button that matches) or a common error or misconception you would like students to discuss (e.g., thinking that only buttons that are exactly the same qualify as matches).

The issue might be logistical (e.g., clarifying the steps of *Button Match-Up* or the Counting Jar or keeping track of who has yet to do the Counting Jar) or management–related (e.g., noise level, working productively, and using, sharing, or caring for materials).

Other alternatives include checking in with students about which activities they have been choosing, having students share a piece of work, or allowing students to raise a question or make a comment about today's math class.

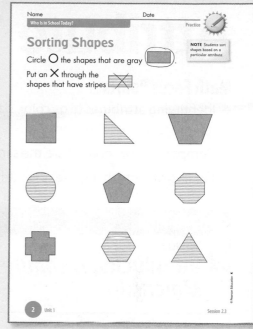

▲ **Student Activity Book, p. 2**

④ SESSION FOLLOW-UP
Practice

Practice: For reinforcement of this unit's content, have students complete *Student Activity Book* page 2.

Attribute Block Match-Up

Math Focus Points

◆ Identifying attributes (e.g., color, size, shape) and developing language to describe them

◆ Comparing how objects are the same and different

◆ Finding objects that share one attribute

Vocabulary

attribute

Today's Plan		Materials
ACTIVITY ① Introducing *Attribute Block Match-Up*	10 MIN CLASS	• Attribute blocks*
MATH WORKSHOP ② Counting and Matching Attributes ②A *Attribute Block Match-Up* ②B *Button Match-Up* ②C Counting Jar ②D Exploring Color Tiles	15–30 MIN	②A • Attribute blocks* ②B • Materials from Session 2.3, p. 70 ②C • Materials from Session 2.1, p. 58 ②D • Materials from Session 1.6, p. 47
DICSUSSION ③ Checking In	5 MIN CLASS	
SESSION FOLLOW-UP ④ Practice		• *Student Math Handbook Flip Chart,* p. 47

*See *Materials to Prepare,* p. 57.

Classroom Routines

Attendance: Breaking Up the Attendance Stick Follow the regular *Attendance* routine, counting the number of students in two ways. Then, as in Session 2.2, ask students to predict what will happen if you give each student one cube from the Attendance Stick. Discuss the number of leftover cubes. (If everyone is present, use this conversation to reinforce the idea that there is one cube for every student.)

ACTIVITY

Introducing *Attribute Block Match-Up*

10 MIN CLASS

Over the last few days, you have had a chance to explore the attribute blocks. What have you found out about them?

Some students may describe what they can be used for (e.g., building and making designs or patterns) and will describe particular things that they made with them. Some will have counted the number of blocks in the set. Others will mention the different attributes. Be sure to discuss each attribute—color, size, and shape—during this conversation.

[Emma] said the blocks are different shapes. [Kyle] said that they are different colors, and [Dennis] said that they are different sizes. All of those things are attributes. An attribute can help you describe something.

Hold up one block.

When I look at this attribute block I notice that this block is blue, shaped like a circle, and larger than some of the other shapes in the box. I think I will call this block the big blue circle.

Hold up a few different blocks in the set and encourage students to name all three attributes—size, color, and shape. ❶

Then, spread out one subset so students can see all of the blocks. Explain that you are going to teach them a new game called *Attribute Block Match-Up*, which is just like *Button Match-Up*. Choose one large block and hold it up.

Teaching Note

❶ **Vocabulary** Students have a wide range of experience with identifying and describing attributes. Many need vocabulary support. Help students form associations by asking questions, such as: *What else do you know that is this color? This shape? What are ways to describe the size of something?*

[Latoya] says that my block is large and red. This shape is called a hexagon. Look at the rest of the shapes I have here. Just like in *Button Match-Up*, your job is to try to find another attribute block that matches in some way; it has something that is the same.

At first, students may be stumped because unlike the buttons the attribute blocks include no exact matches. Point this out to students.

The attribute blocks are different than the buttons. None of these blocks is exactly the same. There is not another large red hexagon. But remember, in this game, two blocks match even if there is just one thing that is the same about them. Do you see another block that has at least one attribute that is the same as this large red hexagon?

Ask several students to choose a block that they think matches your block and to explain why they think so.

[Abby] says that the small red hexagon is a match. [Brad]picked the small red square. Can they *both* be matches? How does [Abby's] match? (It's red *and* it's a hexagon.) What about [Brad's]? (It's red.)

Be sure to discuss several different matches for each block. Understand that some students will think there can only be one match for each block. Some will find it difficult to "see" the match when there is only one thing in common (e.g., the small blue hexagon matches the large red hexagon), and others will think matching blocks can share *only* one attribute. Although negotiating the meaning of rules is important, try to keep the focus on the mathematics—comparing how the blocks are similar and different.

As time permits, follow the same process with another block or two. Then, explain that students can choose to play *Attribute Block Match-Up* in pairs during Math Workshop.

Attribute Block Match-Up works just like *Button Match-Up*. You need a partner and a set of attribute blocks. Take turns picking out one block and then work together to find blocks that match in at least one way.

Remind students about cleaning up the attribute blocks, modeling how to place each block in the proper space as you put them away.

MATH WORKSHOP

Counting and Matching Attributes

15–30 MIN

Explain that the following four activities are available during Math Workshop. Remind students of what each activity entails, what materials are required, and where they are located.

2A *Attribute Block Match-Up*

PAIRS

Students work in pairs to match attribute blocks with at least one attribute that is the same.

Students play Attribute Block Match-Up.

ONGOING ASSESSMENT: Observing Students at Work

Students identify attributes and find objects that share at least one attribute.

- **Are students able to find attribute blocks that share an attribute?** Can they explain how their blocks are the same? What language do they use?

- **Do students focus exclusively on one attribute (e.g., color) or do they consider various attributes (e.g., size, shape, and color)?**

Teaching Note

❷ **When Partners Disagree** Encourage partners who disagree about what qualifies as a match to explain their thinking to each other. You can help by summarizing and explaining how one child sees the two blocks as a match, but know that some students may not yet be ready or able to see that certain blocks match.

DIFFERENTIATION: Supporting the Range of Learners

Intervention Some students may have difficulty focusing on only one attribute. They may think that two blocks do not match unless they are completely or mostly the same. Help them focus on a single attribute by asking them questions, such as:

- How would you describe this block?

- You said this block is a circle. Can you find another block that is a circle?

2B *Button Match-Up*

PAIRS

For complete details about this activity, see Session 2.3, pages 71–72, and consider the following note.

DIFFERENTIATION: Supporting the Range of Learners

Extension Challenge students who find matches easily to find more than one match for a given button or to choose one button and find *all* of the possible matches.

2C Counting Jar

INDIVIDUALS

For complete details about this activity, see Session 2.1, pages 59–60.

2D Exploring Color Tiles

INDIVIDUALS   PAIRS   GROUPS

For complete details about this activity, see Session 1.6, page 50.

DISCUSSION

Checking In

5 MIN   CLASS

Take this opportunity to discuss any issues you noticed while observing students at work. The topic might be mathematical in nature, such as a strategy you would like all students to consider (e.g., finding a match) or a common error or misconception you would like students to discuss (e.g., seeing color as the *only* way to find a match).

The issue might be logistical, such as clarifying the steps of an activity or keeping sets of attribute blocks intact. It might also be management-related, such as being a helpful partner, keeping the noise level down, sharing materials, or working productively. Other alternatives include the following:

- Checking in with students about which activities they have been choosing

- Asking students to share a piece of work

- Allowing students to raise a question or make a comment about today's math class

SESSION FOLLOW-UP

Practice

Student Math Handbook Flip Chart: Use the *Student Math Handbook Flip Chart* page 47 to reinforce concepts from today's session. See pages 144–148 in the back of this unit.

Counting Jar: How Many Did You Find?

Math Focus Points

◆ Developing strategies for accurately counting and keeping track of quantities up to 10

◆ Creating an equivalent set

◆ Comparing how objects are the same and different

Today's Plan		Materials
ACTIVITY ❶ **Attendance: Introducing a Labeled Attendance Stick**	🕐 5–10 MIN 👥 CLASS	• Materials for *Attendance* (from Session 1.1) • Attendance Stick (from Session 1.6) • A labeled Attendance Stick*
MATH WORKSHOP ❷ **Counting and Matching Attributes** **2A** *Attribute Block Match-Up* **2B** *Button Match-Up* **2C** Counting Jar **2D** Exploring Color Tiles	🕐 15–25 MIN	**2A** • Materials from Session 2.4, p. 76 **2B** • Materials from Session 2.3, p. 70 **2C** • Materials from Session 2.1, p. 58 **2D** • Materials from Session 1.6, p. 47
DISCUSSION ❸ **How Many Did You Find?**	🕐 10 MIN 👥 CLASS	• Counting Jar*; a bin of other counters, such as cubes or tiles
SESSION FOLLOW-UP ❹ **Practice and Homework**		• *Student Activity Book,* p. 3 • M3–M4, Family Letter*

*See *Materials to Prepare,* p. 57.

Classroom Routines

Calendar Review the name of the month, the days of the week, and any upcoming special events. Have students help you place the "Today" marker, and count to the number that is today's date. Once the calendar routine is established, many teachers have a rotating calendar helper. While many students willingly take on this role, some need an opportunity to preview what is expected of them before they are willing to lead the class in this routine.

5–10 MIN   CLASS

ACTIVITY

Attendance: Introducing a Labeled Attendance Stick

Do the usual *Attendance* routine—count to determine the number of students present, figure out who is and how many students are absent, and record the information on your recording sheet. Use the Attendance Stick to review the same information.

Here is our Attendance Stick. What does it represent? Yes! It shows the number of students who are in our class when everyone is here. What should I do to make our Attendance Stick show that [Corey] and [Jason] are absent?

[Rebecca] said to take two cubes off. There were 25 cubes in our stick, and I took two cubes off—one for [Corey] and one for [Jason]. How many cubes do you think are in the other part of our Attendance Stick—the part that shows how many students are here today?

Some students remember the total number from counting around the class. Others count the cubes. After gathering ideas, ask students to count as you point to each cube to confirm the number.

So there are 23 cubes in this stick, and there are 23 students in our class today!

Show students the Attendance Stick that you labeled with the numbers one through the total number of students in the class. Explain that because you often break the Attendance Stick into two parts to show the number of students present and absent, you made a stick that you can leave together all the time.

I made *another* Attendance Stick that we can leave together all the time. What do you notice about this stick?

Some students notice that it is about the same length or height as the other stick of present students. Others comment on the stickers on the new stick or the numbers on the stickers.

If this stick should have as many cubes as there are students in our class, how many cubes should it have? Let's count to check.

Count out loud as a class. If students do not notice that the numbers they are saying are on the labels, point this out.

[Mary] said the numbers on the cubes are the numbers we said when we counted. She's right. When we counted the first cube, we said, "One," and the label on this cube is 1.

Count again, connecting the counting words to the written numbers.

Place this Attendance Stick next to the one that shows how many students are present today. Ask students to compare them and comment on what they notice.

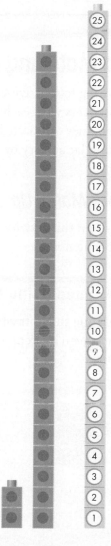

Teaching Note

❶ **Attendance Over Time** Asking students to figure out how many classmates are present or absent provides repeated practice with counting and comparing amounts. Eventually it can encourage reasoning about the total number of students in the class and different ways that a number can be broken into two parts.

Some students may comment on which stick is longer or shorter, how one has stickers and one does not, or on the colors of the cubes. A few may notice that the labeled stick is two cubes taller. They may even connect those two cubes and the two absent students or realize that the number label that is the height of your present-students' tower is the number students got when they took attendance.❶

Students may know that if the cubes for the absent students were added back on to the tower of cubes for the students who are present, the towers would be the same height or length. You might add the cubes back on as an additional comparison.

MATH WORKSHOP

② Counting and Matching Attributes

15–25 MIN

Explain that the following four activities are available during Math Workshop. Remind students what each activity entails, what materials are required, and where they are located. All students need to have completed the Counting Jar activity by the end of this Math Workshop.

. . . .

2A *Attribute Block Match-Up*

PAIRS

For complete details about this activity, see Session 2.4, pages 77–78 and consider the following notes.

DIFFERENTIATION: Supporting the Range of Learners

Extension Challenge students who find matches easily to find more than one match for a given block or to choose one block and find all of the possible matches.

A student tries to find all the possible matches for the large red circle while playing Attribute Block Match-Up.

You can also challenge students to play with a complete set, including thin and thick blocks.

2B *Button Match-Up*

PAIRS

For complete details about this activity, see Session 2.3, pages 71–72.

2C Counting Jar

INDIVIDUALS

For complete details about this activity, see Session 2.1, pages 59–60.

2D Exploring Color Tiles

INDIVIDUALS   PAIRS   GROUPS

For complete details about this activity, see Session 1.6, page 50.

❷ **What's the Answer?** Because there is one right answer, students often are excited to find out what it is. But instead of focusing on the number of objects in the Counting Jar, or on who was right or wrong, keep the emphasis on the strategies used to count and create an equivalent set. In doing so, students see the same answer arising in several ways.

❸ **Who Else Did It That Way?** Asking for a show of hands after each strategy allows many students to participate without each individual sharing.

DISCUSSION

3 How Many Did You Find?

10 MIN   CLASS

Math Focus Points for Discussion

◆ Developing strategies for accurately counting and keeping track of quantities up to 10

◆ Creating an equivalent set

When I was watching you count the bears in our Counting Jar, I noticed that people did it in different ways.❷ Some of you took out one bear at a time as you counted, like this. Raise your hand if you counted like that.❸

I saw other people pour the bears out of the jar to count them. Raise your hand if you did that. Would one of you show us how you counted the bears after you poured them out of the jar?

Did anyone count the bears in a different way?

In this way, model or have students model several different strategies for counting the objects in the jar. Comment on helpful strategies that you see students using.

I noticed that when [Mitchell] counted the bears, he said a number each time he touched a bear, like this.

▲ **Student Activity Book, p. 3**

Once students have demonstrated several strategies for counting and are in agreement on the total number in the jar, ask them about creating an equivalent set. Acknowledge that students used many different materials to create an equivalent set, but focus on the strategies they used to make it.

After you counted the bears in the jar, you made a collection that had the same number of items. How did you make a set that had the same number as there were bears?

Ask volunteers to show how they made an equivalent set using cubes or tiles. There are two main strategies that students use to create an equivalent set and show that it is the same. Some take one cube for each bear, matching them one-to-one. Others recount or remember the number of bears. For example, "There were four bears, so I need four. 1, 2, 3, 4."

So here are our bears, and [Sarah] counted out a set of cubes. Does each group have the same number? How do you know?

Students might say:

"She gave one cube to each bear and there are no more left. Each bear got one."

"There are four bears and four cubes. They are the same. They both have four."

"Look, 1, 2, 3, 4 and 1, 2, 3, 4. They both have four."

SESSION FOLLOW-UP

④ Practice and Homework

 Practice: For reinforcement of this unit's content, have students complete *Student Activity Book* page 3.

 Family Letter: Send home copies of the Family Letter (M3–M4) with each student.

Mathematical Emphases

Counting and Quantity Developing strategies for accurately counting a set of objects by ones

Math Focus Points

- ◆ Developing strategies for accurately counting and keeping track of quantities up to 10

- ◆ Creating an equivalent set

- ◆ Counting, creating, and representing quantities

Data Analysis Sorting and Classifying

Math Focus Points

- ◆ Finding objects that share at least one attribute

- ◆ Using attributes to sort a group of objects

- ◆ Identifying attributes (e.g., color, size, and shape) and developing language to describe them

Data Analysis Carrying Out a Data Investigation

Math Focus Points

- ◆ Collecting and keeping track of survey data

- ◆ Describing and comparing the number of pieces of data in each category

- ◆ Interpreting results of a data investigation

Whole Number Operations Using manipulatives, drawings, tools, and notation to show strategies and solutions

Math Focus Points

- ◆ Representing quantities with pictures, numbers, objects, and/or words

- ◆ Exploring math manipulatives and their attributes

The Today's Question Routine

	Student Activity Book	Student Math Handbook Flip Chart	Professional Development: Read Ahead of Time	
SESSION 3.1 p. 94				
Today's Question The class is introduced to *Today's Question*, a classroom routine in which students respond to a survey question and discuss the resulting data. Math Workshop focuses on comparing the attributes of objects.		44	• **Part 4: Classroom Routines** in *Implementing Investigations in Kindergarten:* Today's Question • **Part 1: Collaborating with the Authors** in *Implementing Investigations in Kindergarten* • **Dialogue Box:** What Do You Notice?, p. 141	
SESSION 3.2 p. 100				
Counting Jar: Recording Students are introduced to a new part of the Counting Jar activity—recording the number of objects in the jar. During Math Workshop, students explore materials, compare attributes, and work on the Counting Jar.		4–10, 20	• **Dialogue Box:** You Could Use Dots, p. 142 • **Teacher Notes:** Counting Is More Than 1, 2, 3, p. 127; Observing Kindergarteners as They Count, p. 135; About Pattern Blocks, p. 128	
SESSION 3.3 p. 106				
Sorting People Students sort people in the class by looking for characteristics that some students have in common. During Math Workshop, students continue to explore materials, compare attributes, and work on the Counting Jar.		20, 47, 48	• **Teacher Note:** Sorting and Identifying Attributes, p. 136	

Classroom Routines See page 16 for an overview.

Calendar	*Attendance*
• Pocket calendar	• Name tags
• "Today" markers	• Attendance Recording Sheet
	• Attendance Stick

Materials to Gather	Materials to Prepare
• **Name tags** (1 per student) • **Markers, crayons, or pencils** (as needed) • **Materials for** *Attribute Block Match-Up* See Session 2.4, p. 76. • **Materials for** *Buttons Match-Up* See Session 2.3, p. 70.	• **Today's Question chart** Write, "Are you a girl or a boy?" at the top of the chart. Label the bottom of one column, "girl," and the bottom of the other column, "boy." See page 95 for an example.
• **M5, Assessment Checklist: Counting** ☑ (from Session 2.1) • **Materials for Counting Jar** See Session 2.1, p. 58. • **Index cards or large self-stick notes** (1 per student plus extras as needed) • **Tape** (as needed) • **Glue** (optional; as needed) • **Materials for Exploring Materials: Pattern Blocks, Geoblocks, Connecting Cubes** See Session 1.1, p. 24. • **Materials for** *Attribute Block Match-Up* See Session 2.4, p. 76.	• **M6–M11, Pattern Block Cut-outs** Make copies of each page onto colored paper. Cut out the individual shapes. Keep like shapes together; store in re-sealable plastic bags. (optional) • **Counting Jar chart or booklets** Create either a Counting Jar chart or a Counting Jar booklet for each student to use to record Counting Jar data. If you make a chart, students record on index cards or large stick-on notes and then place them on the chart. See page 101 for an example. (The chart you create will not yet have stick-on notes on it.) If you make booklets, students record on a separate page each time they do the Counting Jar. See page 102 for an example. • **Counting Jar** Place 6 buttons in the jar for Activity 1; place 5 pencils in the jar for Math Workshop.
• **Materials for the Counting Jar routine** See Session 3.2. • **Materials for Exploring Materials: Pattern Blocks, Geoblocks, Connecting Cubes** See Session 1.1, p. 24. • **Pattern block cut-outs** • **Materials for** *Attribute Block Match-Up* See Session 2.4, p. 76.	

☑ Checklist Available

The Today's Question Routine, *continued*

	Student Activity Book	Student Math Handbook Flip Chart	Professional Development: Read Ahead of Time	
SESSION 3.4 p. 110				
Sorting Attribute Blocks Students sort attribute blocks according to a specific attribute. During Math Workshop, students continue to explore materials, compare attributes, and work on the Counting Jar.		20, 47, 49		
SESSION 3.5 p. 115				
Today's Question: What Did We Find Out? Students sort people by looking for characteristics that some classmates have in common. During Math Workshop, students continue to explore materials, compare attributes, and work on the Counting Jar. After responding to *Today's Question,* they discuss the resulting data.		44, 47		
SESSION 3.6 p. 120				
Counting Jar: How Did You Record? Students sort people by looking for characteristics that some classmates have in common. During Math Workshop, they sort attribute blocks, count sets of objects, and explore materials. Class discussion focuses on how many objects are in the Counting Jar and on how students record what they find.	4			
SESSION 3.7 p. 124				
What Did You Make? Students sort people by looking for characteristics that some classmates have in common. During Math Workshop, students continue to explore materials. They choose one creation to share during the discussion.		49		

Materials to Gather	Materials to Prepare
• **Attribute Blocks** (1 subset per pair) • **Materials for Exploring Materials: Pattern Blocks Geoblocks, Counting Cubes** See Session 1.1, p. 24. • **Pattern block cutouts** • **Materials for the Counting Jar routine** See Session 2.1, p. 58.	• **M12, Attribute Cards** If you are using subsets of attribute blocks, make 4 copies to prepare 4 sets of cards for 4 pairs of students. If you are using full sets of blocks, make 2 copies and 2 sets of cards for 2 pairs of students. Cut apart the cards and use crayons or markers to color the "color" cards. If you have eliminated thick and thin as attributes (by creating subsets), remove these cards from the set. (1 set per pair) • *Today's Question* **chart** Write, "Are you the oldest child in your family?" at the top of the chart. Label the bottom of one column, "Yes," and the bottom of the other column, "No."
• *Today's Question* **chart** from Session 3.4 • **Name tags** (1 per student; from Session 1.1) • **Markers, crayons, or pencils** • **Materials for** *Sorting Attribute Blocks* See Session 3.4. • **Materials for the Counting Jar routine** See Session 3.2. • **Materials for Exploring Materials: Pattern Blocks, Geoblocks, and Connecting Cubes** See Session 1.1, p. 24. • **Pattern block cutouts**	
• **Materials for** *Sorting Attribute Blocks* See Session 3.4 • **Materials for the Counting Jar routine** See Session 2.1, p. 58. • **Materials for Exploring Materials: Pattern Blocks, Geoblocks, and Connecting Cubes** See Session 1.1, p. 24. • **Pattern block cutouts**	
• **Materials for Exploring Materials: Pattern Blocks, Geoblocks, Connecting Cubes** See Session 1.1, p. 24. • **Pattern block cutouts**	

Today's Question

Math Focus Points

- Collecting and keeping track of survey data
- Describing and comparing the number of pieces of data in each category
- Interpreting results of a data investigation

Today's Plan		Materials
ACTIVITY ① **Introducing the *Today's Question* Routine**	5–10 MIN CLASS	• Name tags • *Today's Question* chart: "Are you a girl or a boy?"*
MATH WORKSHOP ② **Matching Attributes** ㉒Ⓐ *Today's Question* ㉒Ⓑ *Attribute Block Match-Up* ㉒Ⓒ *Button Match-Up*	15–25 MIN	Ⓐ • *Today's Question* chart: "Are you a girl or a boy?"* • Name tags; markers, crayons, or pencils (as needed) Ⓑ • Materials from Session 2.4, p. 76 Ⓒ • Materials from Session 2.3, p. 70
DISCUSSION ③ ***Today's Question:* Are You a Girl or a Boy?**	10 MIN CLASS	• Completed *Today's Question* chart: "Are you a girl or a boy?"
SESSION FOLLOW-UP ④ **Practice**		• *Student Math Handbook Flip Chart*, p. 44

*See *Materials to Prepare*, p. 91.

Classroom Routines

Attendance: Comparing with the Attendance Stick Follow the regular *Attendance* routine, counting the number of students in two ways and asking students to help you break the Attendance Stick so that it represents the class today (i.e., one tower representing the number of students present, another representing those that are absent). As they seem ready, encourage students to compare these towers to the numbered Attendance Stick and to describe what they notice.

ACTIVITY

1 Introducing the *Today's Question* Routine

5–10 MIN   CLASS

Show students the *Today's Question* chart: "Are you a girl or a boy?" Explain that during Math Workshop students will respond to a survey question. ❶

During Math Workshop, you are going to answer a question by writing your name on this sheet.

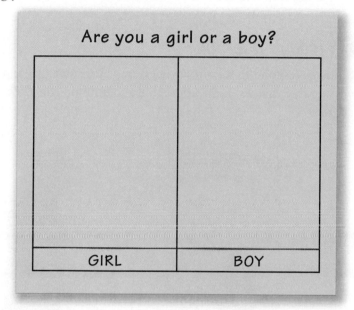

The question is [point to the sheet], "Are you a girl or a boy?" Please don't answer yet!

Talk through the sheet, explaining how students will respond to the survey question.

If you are a girl, you will write your name on this side [point to the left-hand column] where it says, "Girl," and if you are a boy, you will write your name on this side [point to the right-hand column], where it says, "Boy."

Show students the name tags and model how they can use them to figure out how to write their names.

Show students where the *Today's Question* chart and name tags will be located. Talk with students about how they will cycle through this activity, as everyone needs to respond to the question at some point during Math Workshop. Some teachers call one student over at a time, and others have a few respond at a time. ❷ ❸

Teaching Notes

❶ *Today's Question* This routine and the variations suggested throughout the year give students experience with responding to a survey and describing and interpreting survey data. Questions are always provided, but you may prefer to ask different ones that are more timely or significant to your students. However, be sure to choose questions that result in only two responses. For more information, see **Part 4: Classroom Routines** in *Implementing Investigations in Kindergarten:* Today's Question.

❸ *Today's Question* Once established, this routine will not necessarily be a part of Math Workshop. Many teachers have students answer *Today's Question* when they arrive in the morning. Others ask students to respond to the question at some point during the day, before the data is going to be discussed.

Professional Development

❷ **Part 1: Collaborating with the Authors** in *Implementing Investigations in Kindergarten*

Teaching Note

4 **Unorganized Responses** Do not expect students to write their names in an organized manner. As students have repeated opportunities to discuss survey data, this idea will arise as a way to make it easier to compare the data.

MATH WORKSHOP

15–25 MIN

2 Matching Attributes

Explain that the following three activities are available during Math Workshop and that today is the last day that *Button Match-Up* will be available. Remind students what each activity entails, what materials are required, and where they are located. Spend most of your time supporting students as they answer *Today's Question*. All students need to respond before the end of today's Math Workshop, in preparation for the discussion at the end of this session.

2A *Today's Question*

INDIVIDUALS

Students respond to the survey question, "Are you a girl or a boy?" by writing their names in the appropriate column on the *Today's Question* chart. 4

A student responds to Today's Question: "Are you a girl or a boy?"

ONGOING ASSESSMENT: Observing Students at Work

Observe students as they respond to a survey question.

● **Do students understand the question?** Do they record their names in the appropriate column?

DIFFERENTIATION: Supporting the Range of Learners

Intervention As needed, read the words on the *Today's Question* chart aloud to students and help them decide which column to write their name in.

Intervention If there are students who need support writing their names, help them find and use their name tags to figure out how to do it. Encourage students who need a lot of support to write the first letter of their names, and then write the rest for them.

2B Attribute Block Match-Up

PAIRS

For complete details about this activity, see Session 2.4, pages 77–78.

2C Button Match-Up

PAIRS

For complete details about this activity, see Session 2.3, pages 71–72.

DISCUSSION

10 MIN   CLASS

3 Today's Question

Math Focus Points for Discussion

◆ Describing and comparing the number of pieces of data in each category

◆ Interpreting results of a data investigation

Direct students' attention to the completed *Today's Question* chart: "Are you a girl or a boy?" and review the activity. Then ask students to look closely to see what they notice.

Take a minute to and look carefully at our chart. What are some things you notice? ❺

Students will notice a wide range of things, including some things that have little or nothing to do with the data, such as, "The paper is white," or "Some names have *S*'s and some don't." Accept all observations equally, knowing that students learn about how to look at data by having repeated opportunities to do so and by hearing others' comments. Use questions to help students focus on what the data show.

What does this chart tell us about the people in our class?

Professional Development

❺ **Dialogue Box:** What Do You Notice? p. 141

Teaching Notes

❻ Girls and Boys Here Today Establishing one-to-one correspondence between the names on the chart and the number of students present is important. Therefore, focus on the number of students present *today*. You will include absent students later.

❼ Different Counts When more than one student counts, the answers often differ. Students may forget to count themselves, not say one number name for each child, skip or repeat numbers in the sequence, or not count some students. Call students' attention to such discrepancies, but know that many kindergarteners will not respond to them. Focus such discussions on reasons for getting different answers and on strategies for counting accurately rather than on students who counted correctly.

Students may say that it shows some people are girls and some are boys, that there are more boys or girls, or that certain people are girls or boys.

If students do not suggest counting the number of boys and girls, do so now.

I'm interested in finding out how many girls and how many boys there are in our classroom *today*. Who has an idea about how we could find that out?❻

Some students may suggest counting the names on the chart, while others will suggest counting the actual girls and boys. Try all of the ideas that students suggest, reinforcing that double-checking is an important aspect of counting accurately.❼

Next, call students' attention to the fact that the counts were the same, whether you counted children or names on the chart.

We counted the number of girls in our class today and we got [12]. Then we counted the names on the girl side of the chart and we got [12]. We got the same number. Why do you think that happened?

After discussing both the girl and boy counts, ask students to compare the quantities.

We found out that there are [12] girls and [10] boys here today. Are there *more* boys or girls here today? How do you know?

Finally, re-establish how many students are in class today and compare that number to the total number of names on the chart.

When we took attendance today, there were [22] students in school [hold up today's Attendance Stick]. If we count all of the names on this chart, how many do you think there will be?

After students share their ideas, count the names on the chart together as a group.

There are [22] names on the chart and [22] students in school today. Does it surprise you that those two numbers are the same?

Listen for explanations that suggest students understand that the number of students in the class corresponds to the number of students who wrote their names on the chart. Because using names to represent people is slightly abstract, some students may not yet make this connection.

Again, refer back to today's attendance data to add absent students to your chart.

The class discusses how the number of students they counted during Attendance *is the same as the total number of names on the* Today's Question *chart.*

Not everyone in our class is here today. [Lisa], [Hugo], and [Raul] are absent today—[1 girl] and [2 boys]. We counted and found out that there are 12 girls in our class today, but we didn't count [Lisa]. How many girls are there in our class when everyone is here? What about the boys?

After adding the names of absent students to the chart, count the total number of names on the chart and relate this information to the class Attendance Stick.

We counted the names of all the boys and all the girls in our class, and we found that there were [25] students in all. Let's take a look at our Attendance Stick. Who remembers how many cubes are in our stick? Let's count them to make sure they are all there.

Encourage students to count as you point to each cube, counting both the students who are present and absent.

SESSION FOLLOW-UP
4 Practice

Student Math Handbook Flip Chart: Use the *Student Math Handbook Flip Chart* page 44 to reinforce concepts from today's session. See pages 144–148 in the back of this unit.

Counting Jar: Recording

Math Focus Points

◆ Developing strategies for accurately counting and keeping track of quantities up to 10

◆ Creating an equivalent set

◆ Representing quantities with pictures, numbers, and/or words

Today's Plan		Materials
ACTIVITY ① **Counting Jar: Introducing Recording**	🕐 10 MIN 👥 CLASS	• Counting Jar* • Class Counting Jar chart, or a Counting Jar booklet*
MATH WORKSHOP ② **Counting, Recording, and Exploring Materials** ②A Counting Jar: Recording ②B Exploring Materials: Pattern Blocks, Geoblocks, and Connecting Cubes ②C *Attribute Block Match-Up*	🕐 15–30 MIN	②A • Materials from Activity 1; M5 (from Session 2.1) ②B • Materials from Session 1.1, p. 24 • M6–M11* ②C • Materials from Session 2.4, p. 76
DISCUSSION ③ **Checking In**	🕐 5 MIN 👥 CLASS	
SESSION FOLLOW-UP ④ **Practice**		• *Student Math Handbook Flip Chart*, pp. 4–10, 20

*See *Materials to Prepare*, p. 91.

Classroom Routines

Calendar Review the name of the month, the days of the week, and any upcoming special events. Have students, or the calendar helper, help you place the "Today" marker and count to the number that is today's date.

Professional Development

❶ **Dialogue Box:** You Could Use Dots, p. 142

ACTIVITY

① Counting Jar: Introducing Recording

10 MIN CLASS

Explain that students are going to revisit the Counting Jar today, but that this time there will be another step. Show students the Counting Jar with six buttons in it.

Just like last time, you are going to count the objects that are in the jar and make a collection with that same number. But today there is a new step. You are also going to show on a piece of paper how many objects are in the jar.

Ask several volunteers to count the buttons. Once you are in agreement on the total, brainstorm ways that students could show that information on paper.❶

We agree that there are six buttons in the Counting Jar. How could we show on a piece of paper that there are six buttons in the jar? Who has a different idea?

Expect students to suggest some combination of pictures (circles, pictures of buttons, or slash marks), numbers (6), and words (buttons). Model places in the classroom where students can look to figure out how to write a number they do not know yet, such as the numbers on the Counting Jar chart, the calendar, or a number line. Model each idea that a student suggests on an index card or slip of paper labeled with the student's name.

If you are using the Counting Jar chart, post each example on it, modeling how students will tape their responses to the chart or put up their self-stick notes. If students will be using Counting Jar booklets, demonstrate this instead.

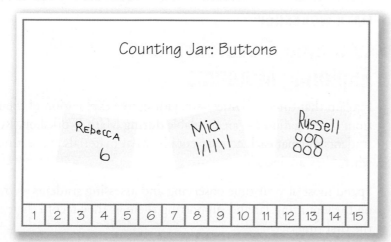

❷ **Assembling a Portfolio** Because students do Counting Jar in every unit, it provides an opportunity to see students' growth over time. Therefore, you might want to copy students' completed work on this Counting Jar and put it in their portfolios.

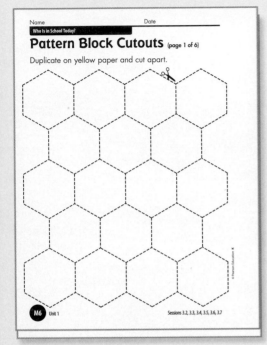

Name _____ Date _____

Who Is in School Today?

Pattern Block Cutouts (page 1 of 6)

Duplicate on yellow paper and cut apart.

M6 Unit 1   Sessions 3.2, 3.3, 3.4, 3.5, 3.6, 3.7

▲ **Resource Masters, M6–M7**

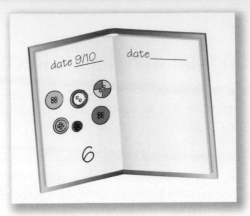

date 9/10   date_____

6

You have a lot of ideas about how to show that there are six buttons in our Counting Jar! When you record, you can use one of these ideas or a different idea.

Finally, review and model how to make an equivalent set.

Just like last time, you also need to make a collection of things. Your collection must have the same number of objects you found in the jar. We counted six buttons, so I would count out six [cubes], six [pattern blocks], or six [tiles] and put them in my bag. [Demonstrate.]

Explain that you are going to put a different set of objects in the jar for Math Workshop and summarize the three steps:

- Count

- Record and tape your representation on the Counting Jar chart or record in your Counting Jar booklet❷

- Create an equivalent set

MATH WORKSHOP

15–30 MIN

2 Counting, Recording, and Exploring Materials

Explain that three activities—including free exploration of the materials from Investigation 1—are available during Math Workshop. Remind students of what each activity entails, what materials are required, and where they are located.

Spend most of your time observing and assessing students as they work on the Counting Jar and supporting them as they record their count for the first time.

2A Counting Jar: Recording

INDIVIDUALS

Students count the objects in the Counting Jar, record the amount on either the Counting Jar chart or their Counting Jar booklets, and make a set of the same size.❸ ❹

ONGOING ASSESSMENT: Observing Students at Work

Observe students as they count a set of objects, record their count, and create an equivalent set.❺

- **How familiar are students with the sequence of number names?** Do they omit, repeat, or mix the order of some numbers? Which ones?

- **How do students count the objects in the jar?** Do they remove and count one object at a time or empty the jar and count the objects as they put them back in? Do they dump the jar and then count the objects? Do they organize the objects in some way? Do they touch or move each item as they count it? Do any students double-check their count?

- **How do students represent the contents of the jar?** Do they use pictures or symbols (e.g., circles or slash marks) to represent the objects? If so, do they draw one for each object or do they draw five pictures because they counted five objects? Do they use numbers? How do they figure out how to write a particular number?

- **How do students create an equivalent set?** Do they count out the quantity (e.g., "There are five pencils, so I need five cubes.")? Do they take one counter for each pencil? (Note: Students who use this strategy can create an equivalent set without counting.)

- **Once finished, do students compare their sets to the set in the jar?** How do they decide whether the sets are the same?

Professional Development

❸ **Teacher Note:** Counting Is More Than 1, 2, 3, p. 127

❹ **Teacher Note:** Observing Kindergarteners as They Count, p. 135

Teaching Note

❺ **Observing Students' Counting** Continue to use the Counting Jar activity to get a sense of students' familiarity and comfort with the counting sequence and the process of counting. Add new observations on the Assessment Checklist: Counting (M5).

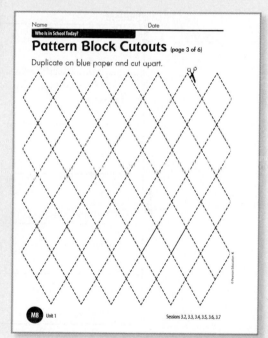

▲ Resource Masters, M8

Professional Development

⑥ **Teacher Note:** About Pattern Blocks, p. 128

DIFFERENTIATION: Supporting the Range of Learners

Intervention Students who do not have strong small-motor coordination can use a stamp to show the quantity on paper. Because it is fun to use stamps, students may need help remembering to stamp only the quantity in the jar—rather than filling the whole page with stamps.

For more intervention suggestions for this activity, see Session 2.1, page 62.

Assessment Checklist: Counting ✓

Student	Knows the names of the numbers in order	Counts each object once and only once	Has a system for keeping track	Double-checks	Notes
Hugo	✓ to 10	no, doesn't take out pencils, recites #s from 1–10, doesn't point	no, not attaching #s to objects		draws many lines on paper
Shavonne	✓ to 5	takes each pencil out, says 1 # per pencil	maybe? pencils in jar haven't counted. outside jar have counted	no	draws 5 pencils, lots of details
Kiyo	no, skips 3	yes, but skips 3 so gets 6	puts pencils in 2 lines	no	practice counting with her?
Mitchell	✓ to 10	says 1 # per object but loses track of which counted so says there are 8	no, pencils scattered on table, points but doesn't organize	no	suggest that M. watch Brad count and keep track?
Carmen	✓ to 20	yes	yes, takes all pencils out, moves them to new pile as she counts	no	writes 5 and draws 5 lines

 INDIVIDUALS PAIRS GROUPS

2B Exploring Materials: Pattern Blocks, Geoblocks, and Connecting Cubes

For complete details about these activities, see Session 1.1, pages 28–31, and consider the following note.

DIFFERENTIATION: Supporting the Range of Learners

Extension Students who are interested in recording their pattern block work can glue Pattern Block Cutouts (M6–M11) onto paper or cardstock.⑥

2C *Attribute Block Match-Up* **PAIRS**

For complete details about this activity, see Session 2.4, pages 77–78.

DISCUSSION
3 Checking In

5 MIN   CLASS

Take this opportunity to discuss any issues that you noticed while observing students at work. The topic might be mathematical in nature, such as a strategy you would like all students to consider (e.g., ways to make sure your equivalent set has the same number of objects as there are in the Counting Jar) or a common error or misconception you would like students to discuss (e.g., saying more than one number per object when counting).

It could also be a logistical issue, such as clarifying the steps to the Counting Jar activity or a management issue, such as using, sharing, and/or caring for materials, keeping the noise level down, or working productively.

A student shares a tower that he built while exploring Geoblocks.

SESSION FOLLOW-UP
4 Practice

 Student Math Handbook Flip Chart: Use the *Student Math Handbook Flip Chart* pages 4–10, 20 to reinforce concepts from today's session. See pages 144–148 in the back of this unit.

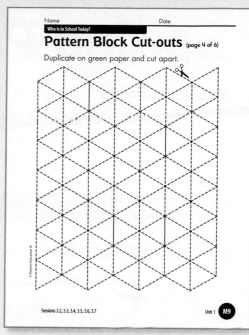

▲ **Resource Masters, M9**

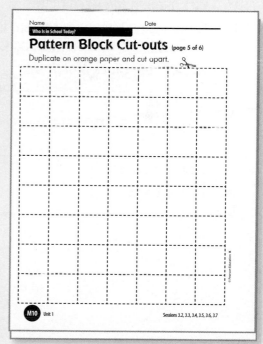

▲ **Resource Masters, M10–M11**

Sorting People

Math Focus Points

◆ Finding objects that share at least one attribute

◆ Exploring math manipulatives and their attributes

◆ Counting, creating, and representing quantities

Today's Plan		Materials
ACTIVITY ① **Sorting People**	10–15 MIN CLASS	
MATH WORKSHOP ② **Counting, Recording, and Exploring Materials** **2A** Counting Jar: Recording **2B** Exploring Materials: Pattern Blocks, Geoblocks, and Connecting Cubes **2C** *Attribute Block Match-Up*	15–25 MIN	**2A** • Materials from Session 3.2, p. 100 **2B** • Materials from Session 1.1, p. 24 • Pattern block cutouts **2C** • Materials from Session 2.4, p. 76
DISCUSSION ③ **Checking In**	5 MIN CLASS	
SESSION FOLLOW-UP ④ **Practice**		• *Student Math Handbook Flip Chart*, pp. 20, 47, 48

Classroom Routines

Attendance: Comparing with the Attendance Stick Follow the regular *Attendance* routine, counting the number of students in two ways and asking students to help you break the Attendance Stick so that it represents the class today (e.g., one tower representing the number of students present, another representing those that are absent). If students seem ready, encourage them to compare these towers to the numbered Attendance Stick and to describe what they notice.

ACTIVITY

Sorting People

10–15 MIN CLASS

Introduce this activity by choosing a characteristic that is visually obvious about some of the students in your class, such as "has black hair" or "has striped shirt." ❶

I noticed today that there is something the same about some of you, but not all of you. Some people are [wearing shorts]. Let's see how many people are [wearing shorts].

Ask all of the students who are wearing shorts to stand next to you; the rest should remain seated. If any students are not sure whether they have the characteristic you chose, discuss it as a class.

The class sorts students by whether they are wearing shorts.

These students are all [wearing shorts]. Let's count them [lead the class in counting]. There are [6] people [wearing shorts] today. If we describe this group as the [Students Wearing Shorts Group], then what can you say about the students who are not standing next to me?

Some students will name characteristics that are related to your chosen characteristic, such as wearing pants, wearing skirts, or wearing dresses. Others may see different things that some or many of the seated children have in common, such as wearing sneakers, having brown hair, or wearing glasses.

So, we can make other groups like [wearing long pants] and [wearing skirts]. We could also call this group [Students Who Are Not Wearing Shorts]. ❷

MATH WORKSHOP

Counting, Recording, and Exploring Materials

15–25 MIN

Explain that three activities are available during Math Workshop, and that today is the last day that *Attribute Block Match-Up* will be available. Remind students of what each activity entails, what materials are required, and where they are located.

2A Counting Jar: Recording

INDIVIDUALS

For complete details about this activity, see Session 3.2, pages 101–102.

2B Exploring Materials: Pattern Blocks, Geoblocks, and Connecting Cubes

INDIVIDUALS PAIRS GROUPS

For complete details about these activities, see Session 1.1, pages 28–31. Have available pattern block cutouts for students who want to record their creations.

2C *Attribute Block Match-Up*

PAIRS

For complete details about this activity, see Session 2.4, pages 77–78.❸

DISCUSSION
Checking In

5 MIN   CLASS

Take this opportunity to discuss any issues that you noticed while observing students at work. The topic might be mathematical in nature, such as a strategy you would like all students to consider (e.g., different ways students have been exploring the materials) or a common error or misconception you would like students to discuss (e.g., recording what was in the jar, but not the quantity they found in the jar).

It could also be a logistical issue (e.g., remembering to write names on Counting Jar representations or how to post representations on the chart) or a management issue, such as returning materials after finishing an activity.

SESSION FOLLOW-UP
Practice

Student Math Handbook Flip Chart: Use the *Student Math Handbook Flip Chart* pages 20, 47, 48 to reinforce concepts from today's session. See pages 144–148 in the back of this unit.

Sorting Attribute Blocks

Math Focus Points

◆ Using attributes to sort a group of objects

◆ Identifying attributes (e.g., color, size, and shape) and developing language to describe them

◆ Counting, creating, and representing quantities

Today's Plan			Materials
ACTIVITY ① **Introducing** *Sorting Attribute Blocks*	🕐 5–10 MIN	👥 CLASS	• M12* • Attribute blocks
MATH WORKSHOP ② **Counting, Sorting, and Exploring** ②A *Sorting Attribute Blocks* ②B Counting Jar: Recording ②C Exploring Materials: Pattern Blocks, Geoblocks, and Connecting Cubes	🕐 20–30 MIN		②A • Materials from Activity 1 ②B • Materials from Session 3.2, p. 100 ②C • Materials from Session 1.1, p. 24 • Pattern block cutouts
ACTIVITY ③ *Today's Question:* **Are You the Oldest Child in Your Family?**	🕐 5–10 MIN	👥 CLASS	• *Today's Question* chart*
SESSION FOLLOW-UP ④ **Practice**			• *Student Math Handbook Flip Chart*, pp. 20, 47, 49

*See *Materials to Prepare,* p. 93.

Classroom Routines

Calendar Review the name of the month, the days of the week, and any upcoming special events. Have students, or the calendar helper, help you place the "Today" marker, and count to the number that is today's date.

ACTIVITY

1 Introducing *Sorting Attribute Blocks*

5–10 MIN CLASS

Yesterday we sorted people. We looked for ways that some people were the same. During Math Workshop today, you are going to play a new game called *Sorting Attribute Blocks*. When you play *Sorting Attribute Blocks*, you look for attribute blocks that are the same. You and your partner will take turns picking a card that tells you how to sort the blocks.

Spread out a set of attribute blocks and show students one of the Attribute Cards (M12), for example, the yellow card.

What do you think this card says? (*yellow*) Yes, it says yellow. Let's find all of the yellow attribute blocks and put them all over here [point to a location in the classroom].

Do you think we have all of the yellow blocks? How can you tell?

So, over here [point to yellow blocks] we have all of the yellow attribute blocks. And over here [point to the rest of the blocks] we have all the attribute blocks that are *not* yellow.

Choose another card, one that shows a different attribute, such as shape or size, and ask students to help you find all the blocks that match it.

MATH WORKSHOP

2 Counting, Sorting, and Exploring

20–30 MIN

Explain that three activities are available during Math Workshop. Remind students of what each activity entails, what materials are required, and where they are located.

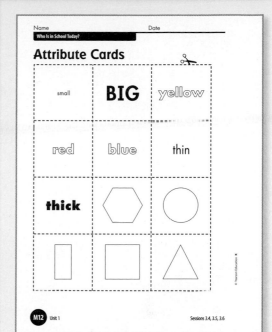

▲ **Resource Masters, M12**

2A Sorting Attribute Blocks

PAIRS

Pairs take turns picking an attribute card and sorting the blocks according to the attribute on the card.

Students play Sorting Attribute Blocks.

ONGOING ASSESSMENT: Observing Students at Work

Students sort objects according to their attributes.

- **Can students tell what attribute is shown on the card?** Can they find blocks with that attribute? Are students more confident with some attributes than with others (e.g., colors over shapes)?

- **How clearly can students communicate about the attributes and the blocks under consideration?** What words do they use?

- **Do students try to find *all* the blocks that fit a given attribute?** How do they know and explain that they have them all?

DIFFERENTIATION: Supporting the Range of Learners

Intervention Some students may benefit from playing with a smaller set of blocks. You can either limit the set (e.g., remove the yellow card and all of the yellow blocks) or encourage students to divide the blocks so students consider half the blocks as they play.

2B Counting Jar: Recording

INDIVIDUALS

For complete details about this activity, see Sessions 3.2, pages 101–102.

2C Exploring Materials: Pattern Blocks, Geoblocks, and Connecting Cubes

INDIVIDUALS PAIRS GROUPS

For complete details about these activities, see Session 1.1, pages 28–31. Have available pattern block cutouts for students who want to record their creations.

ACTIVITY

5–10 MIN CLASS

3 Today's Question: Are You the Oldest Child in Your Family?

Show students the *Today's Question* chart with the new question on it.

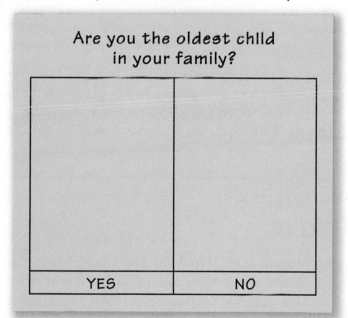

The other day, you answered the question, "Are you a boy or a girl?" and we talked about what we found out. We are going to do a lot of surveys this year to find out more about our class. Every few days, I am going to write a new question, and your job will be to respond to it.

Teaching Note

❶ **But I'm the** *Only* **Child** Students who are only children may be unsure about how to respond. Help them see that even though they are "the only child," they are also the "oldest" because there are no children older than they are in their families.

Explain how this routine will work in your classroom. Options include having students respond when they arrive in the morning, during Math Workshop, or whenever they have time during the day. Remind students that their name tags are always available to help them with writing their names.

[When you arrive tomorrow], you will answer this question: "Are you the oldest child in your family?" This column says, "Yes," and this column says, "No" [point to each respective column on the chart]. Think about the question tonight and then tomorrow you will write your name above "Yes" or "No."❶

DIFFERENTIATION: Supporting the Range of Learners

ELL English Language Learners may need support with the *Today's Question* routine. One-on-one or in a small group, show students a family photograph or a simple drawing that includes a mother, a father, and at least three children of clearly different ages.

There are three children in this family. Some of them are younger and some are older. [Point to the largest child.] This is the oldest child in the family. I can tell he's the oldest child because he's the biggest one.

Have children repeat the word *oldest* after you. Then, using the picture as reference, ask each student whether he or she is the *oldest* child in his or her family. English Language Learners may need this kind of visual support with other survey questions as well.

SESSION FOLLOW-UP
Practice

Student Math Handbook Flip Chart: Use to *Student Math Handbook Flip Chart* pages 20, 47, 49 to reinforce concepts from today's session. See pages 144–148 in the back of this unit.

Today's Question: What Did We Find Out?

Math Focus Points

◆ Finding objects that share at least one attribute

◆ Describing and comparing the number of pieces of data in each category

◆ Interpreting results of a data investigation

Today's Plan		Materials
ACTIVITY ❶ **Sorting People**	🕐 10 MIN CLASS	
MATH WORKSHOP ❷ **Counting, Sorting, and Exploring** **2A** *Today's Question:* **Are You the Oldest Child in Your Family?** **2B** *Sorting Attribute Blocks* **2C** Counting Jar: Recording **2D** Exploring Materials: Pattern Blocks, Geoblocks, and Connecting Cubes	🕐 10–25 MIN	**2A** • *Today's Question* chart from Session 3.4 • Name tags; markers, crayons, or pencils **2B** • Materials from Session 3.4, p. 110 **2C** • Materials from Session 3.2, p. 100 **2D** • Materials from Session 1.1, p. 24 • Pattern block cutouts
DISCUSSION ❸ **Today's Question: Are You the Oldest Child in Your Family?**	🕐 10 MIN CLASS	• *Today's Question* chart from Activity 2A
SESSION FOLLOW-UP ❹ **Practice**		• *Student Math Handbook Flip Chart*, pp. 44, 47

Classroom Routines

Attendance: Comparing with the Attendance Stick Follow the routine, counting the number of students in two ways. Ask students to help break the Attendance Stick so that it represents the number of students present and absent. Encourage students to compare the towers to the Attendance Stick and to describe what they notice.

ACTIVITY

1 Sorting People

10 MIN   CLASS

Choose a characteristic that some—but not all—students have in common, such as curly hair or wearing sneakers.

The other day I noticed that some of you were [wearing shorts] and some of you were not. You helped me sort the class into two groups— [Students Wearing Shorts] and [Students Not Wearing Shorts]. Today I noticed that some of you are [wearing sneakers]. Let's sort our class into two groups. Can everyone who is [wearing sneakers] stand next to me?

Count the number of students who are wearing sneakers and the number who are not, and name both groups.

So eight students are wearing sneakers.

And 11 students are not wearing sneakers.

Sort students in the class one or two more times using different characteristics.

MATH WORKSHOP

2 Counting, Sorting, and Exploring

10–25 MIN

Explain that three activities—or four if you have not already asked students to respond to *Today's Question*—are available during Math Workshop. Remind students of what each activity entails, what materials are required, and where they are located. All students need to have answered *Today's Question* by the end of Math Workshop.

2A Today's Question: Are You the Oldest Child in Your Family?

INDIVIDUALS

For complete details about this activity, see Session 3.4, pages 113–114.

2B Sorting Attribute Blocks

PAIRS

For complete details about this activity, see Session 3.4, page 111, and consider the following note.

DIFFERENTIATION: Supporting the Range of Learners

Extension Students who are ready for more of a challenge can select two cards at a time and find all of the blocks that have the two attributes. For example, they can find the blocks that are both small *and* red.

2C Counting Jar: Recording

INDIVIDUALS

For complete details about this activity, see Session 3.2, pages 101–102.

2D Exploring Materials: Pattern Blocks, Geoblocks, and Connecting Cubes

INDIVIDUALS PAIRS GROUPS

For complete details about these activities, see Session 1.1, pages 28–31. Have available pattern block cut-outs for students who want to record their creations.

DISCUSSION

3 Today's Question: Are You the Oldest Child in Your Family?

10 MIN CLASS

Math Focus Points for Discussion

◆ Interpreting results of a data investigation

◆ Describing and comparing the number of pieces of data in each category

Post the *Today's Question* chart so that all students can see it. Review the question and ask students to look carefully at the survey data.

Our survey question was, "Are you the oldest child in your family?" Here are all of your responses. [Point to the chart.] What do you notice about the data?

Some students point out their own name or another student's. Others comment on which column has more or count the number of responses in each column. They also may make remarks that are not connected to the data. Accept all responses, but then ask students to comment on what the data show.

What did we learn about the students who are here today and whether or not they are the oldest child in their families?

Some students will say that some are the oldest and some are not. Others will be more specific, saying whether more students are or are not the oldest. If they do not talk about the number of students in each category, bring this up yourself.

Of the students who are here today, how many are the oldest child in their family?

Count together the number of students who wrote their names under "Yes" and record that number at the top of the column.

Of the students who are here today, how many are *not* the oldest child in their family?

Count the number under "No" and record it.

Are there more students who are the oldest child in their family [run your hand down the list of names in that column] or more students who are not the oldest child in their family [run your hand down the list of names in that column]? How do you know?

Some students will reason about the numbers or quantities.

Students might say:

"Eleven are the oldest kids, and 8 are not the oldest kids, and 11 is bigger than 8."

Others will compare the length of the lists of names or the amount of space they take up.

How many people answered our survey question today? How can we find out?

Some students may count the number of responses in each column or the number of people present. Others may remember the number of students present today or say that you can take the number of students and take away the number absent. Try each of the ways that students suggest and then record the number at the bottom of the sheet.

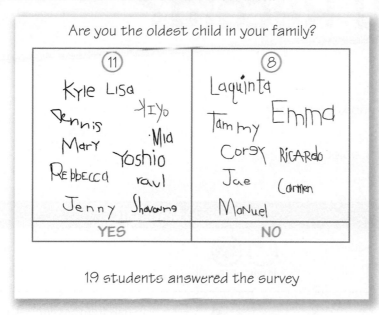

Are you the oldest child in your family?

⑪	⑧
Kyle Lisa ᠈IYo Dennis Mary ·Mia Yoshio Rebbecca raul Jenny Shavaune	Laquinta Tammy Emma Corey Ricardo Jae Carmen Manuel
YES	NO

19 students answered the survey

SESSION FOLLOW-UP
Practice

Student Math Handbook Flip Chart: Use the *Student Math Handbook Flip Chart* pages 44, 47 to reinforce concepts from today's session. See pages 144–148 in the back of this unit.

Counting Jar: How Did You Record?

Math Focus Points

◆ Finding objects that share at least one attribute

◆ Developing strategies for accurately counting and keeping track of quantities up to 10

◆ Representing quantities with pictures, numbers, objects, and/or words

Today's Plan		Materials
ACTIVITY ❶ **Sorting People**	10 MIN CLASS	
MATH WORKSHOP ❷ **Counting, Sorting, and Exploring** ⓐ *Sorting Attribute Blocks* ⓑ Counting Jar: Recording ⓒ Exploring Materials: Pattern Blocks, Geoblocks, and Connecting Cubes	10–25 MIN	ⓐ • Materials from Session 3.4, p. 110 ⓑ • Materials from Session 3.2, p. 100 ⓒ • Materials from Session 1.1, p. 24 • Pattern block cutouts
DISCUSSION ❸ **How Did You Record?**	10 MIN CLASS	• Counting Jar chart or booklets
SESSION FOLLOW-UP ❹ **Practice**		• *Student Activity Book*, p. 4

Classroom Routines

Calendar Determine as a class today's date and mark it on the class calendar. Count the numbers aloud from 1 to today's date as you point to them on the calendar.

ACTIVITY

1 Sorting People

10 MIN CLASS

Ask students to look carefully at their classmates to see whether they can find something that some—but not all—of them have in common. Ask a student who notices something to whisper it in your ear.❶

A student whispers to the teacher a characteristic that some of his classmates have in common.

[Jae] noticed that some of you have [brown hair]. Anyone who has [brown hair] come stand next to me.

How many students are there with [brown hair]? What can we say about the students *not* standing next to me?❷

Using students' ideas, sort the students in the class one or two more times.

MATH WORKSHOP

2 Counting, Sorting, and Exploring

10–25 MIN

Explain that three activities are available during Math Workshop. Remind students what each activity entails, what materials are required, and where they are located. All students need to have done the Counting Jar activity by the end of today's Math Workshop.

Teaching Notes

❶ **Dealing with Sensitive Issues** Be sensitive to any physical attributes that might make a child feel singled out or uncomfortable.

❷ **Language and Sorting** Identifying attributes and describing what is the same about a group of people or objects includes a significant language component. Oftentimes, students can sort objects correctly because they can visually identify a common attribute, but they have difficulty naming the attribute or naming the group as a whole. The activities in this Investigation include many opportunities for students to use language to describe attributes and to discuss what is the same and different about sets of objects and data.

2A Sorting Attribute Blocks

PAIRS

For complete details about this activity, see Session 3.4, page 111.

2B Counting Jar: Recording

INDIVIDUALS

For complete details about this activity, see Session 3.2, pages 101–102.

2C Exploring Materials: Pattern Blocks, Geoblocks, and Connecting Cubes

INDIVIDUALS PAIRS GROUPS

For complete details about these activities, see Session 1.1, pages 28–31. Have available pattern block cutouts for students who want to record their creations.

DISCUSSION

10 MIN CLASS

3 How Did You Record?

Math Focus Points for Discussion

◆ Representing quantities with pictures, numbers, objects, and/or words

Place the Counting Jar chart with students' representations taped on it so everyone can see them. Or, if students recorded in individual Counting Jar booklets, ask them to bring them to the discussion and to open them to the appropriate page.

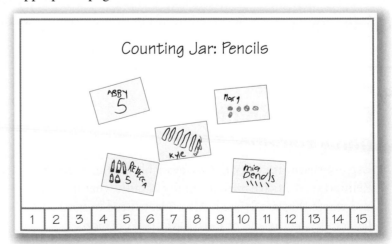

Ask the students how many pencils they found in the Counting Jar. Have several students count the pencils and then count them as a class to double-check. Remember to focus most of this discussion on the different ways students represented the contents of the Counting Jar.

Take a minute to look at the different ways students showed how many pencils were in the Counting Jar.

After students have had a minute to consider the variety of representations, have them focus on a particular strategy for recording.

I noticed that some people drew pictures of pencils to show that there were five pencils in the jar [point out these representations]. Raise your hand if you drew pictures of pencils. ❸

Other people used lines to show how many. Who used lines? Some other people used numbers. How many of you wrote numbers? Some people used pictures and numbers. Who drew pictures and wrote numbers? These are all good ways of showing the number of objects in the Counting Jar.

SESSION FOLLOW-UP

Practice

Practice: For enrichment, have students complete *Student Activity Book,* page 4.

Teaching Note

❸ **Who Did It This Way?** Asking students to raise their hands if they used a particular method of recording allows many students to participate without using the time it takes to have each student share.

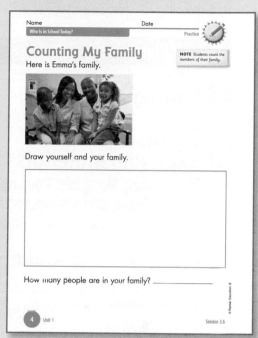

Name _____ Date _____
Who Is in School Today?   Practice

Counting My Family
Here is Emma's family.

NOTE Students count the members of their family.

Draw yourself and your family.

How many people are in your family? _____

4 Unit 1   Session 3.6

▲ **Student Activity Book, p. 4**

What Did You Make?

Math Focus Points

◆ Finding objects that share at least one attribute

◆ Exploring math manipulatives and their attributes

Today's Plan		Materials
① ACTIVITY **Sorting People** ⏱ 10 MIN 👥 CLASS		
② MATH WORKSHOP **Exploring Materials** ⏱ 10–25 MIN **②A Exploring Materials: Pattern Blocks, Geoblocks, and Connecting Cubes**		**②A** • Materials from Session 1.1, p. 24 • Pattern block cutouts
③ DISCUSSION **What Did You Make?** ⏱ 10 MIN 👥 CLASS		• Students' creations from Math Workshop
④ SESSION FOLLOW-UP **Practice**		• *Student Math Handbook Flip Chart*, p. 49

Classroom Routines

Attendance: Comparing with the Attendance Stick Follow the regular *Attendance* routine, counting the number of students in two ways and asking students to help you break the Attendance Stick so that it represents the class today (e.g., one tower representing the number of students present, another representing those that are absent). As they seem ready, encourage students to compare these towers to the numbered Attendance Stick and to describe what they notice.

ACTIVITY
① Sorting People

10 MIN   CLASS

Again, ask students to look carefully at their classmates to see whether they can find something that some—but not all—of them have in common. Ask a student who notices something, but did not share an idea last time, to whisper the idea in your ear.

Have the student announce what he or she noticed. Then ask students to help sort the students into two groups—those who have that characteristic and those who do not. Name the groups and count the number of students in each group.

Using students' ideas, sort people in the class one or two more times.

MATH WORKSHOP
② Exploring Materials

10–25 MIN

Explain that this activity is available during Math Workshop. Remind students what the activity entails, what materials are required and where they are located. Explain that they need to save one thing they make to share with the class at the end of the session.

INDIVIDUALS   PAIRS   GROUPS

②A Exploring Materials: Pattern Blocks, Geoblocks, and Connecting Cubes

For complete details about this activity, see Session 1.1, pages 28–31. Have available pattern block cutouts for students who want to record their creations.

Students make designs with pattern block cutouts.

DISCUSSION

③ What Did You Make?

10 MIN CLASS

Math Focus Points for Discussion

◆ Exploring math manipulatives and their attributes

Students can bring their creations to the meeting area on trays or sturdy cardboard work mats. Or, they can leave them intact at their workspace, and the class can tour the room, viewing the creations as if they were in a museum.

Who made something with Geoblocks?

A student shares one thing about her Geoblock construction.

Have each of these students say one thing about their creations. Do the same for each material.

 SESSION FOLLOW-UP

④ Practice

 Student Math Handbook Flip Chart: Use the *Student Math Handbook Flip Chart* page 49 to reinforce concepts from today's session. See pages 144–148 in the back of this unit.

Counting Is More Than 1, 2, 3

Counting is the basis for understanding our number system and for almost all of the number work in the primary grades. It involves more than just knowing the number names, their sequence, and how to write each number. While it may seem simple, counting is actually quite complex and involves the interplay between a number of skills and concepts.

Rote Counting

Students need to know the number names and their order by rote; they learn this sequence—both forward and backward—by hearing others count and by counting themselves. However, just as saying the alphabet does not indicate that a student can use written language, being able to say "one, two, three, four, five, six, seven, eight, nine, ten" does not necessarily indicate that students know what those counting words mean. Students also need to use numbers in meaningful ways if they are to build an understanding of quantity and number relationships.

One-to-One Correspondence

To count accurately, a student must know that one number name stands for one object that is being counted. Often, when young children first begin to count, they do not connect the numbers in the "counting song" to the objects they are counting. Children learn about one-to-one correspondence through repeated opportunities to count sets of objects and to watch others as they count. One-to-one correspondence develops over time with students first counting small groups of objects (up to five or six) accurately, and eventually larger groups.

Keeping Track

Another important part of counting accurately is being able to keep track of what has already been counted and what remains to be counted. As students first learn to count sets of objects, they often count some objects more than once and skip other objects altogether. Students develop strategies for organizing and keeping track of a count as they realize the need and as they see others use such strategies.

Connecting Numbers to Quantities

Many young students are still coordinating the ordinal sequence of the numbers with the cardinal meaning of those numbers. In other words, we get to 5 by counting in order 1, 2, 3, 4, 5. Understanding this aspect of number is connected to the one-to-one correspondence between the numbers we say and the objects we are counting. However, being able to count accurately using this ordinal sequence is not the same as knowing that when we have finished counting, the final number in our sequence will tell us the quantity of the things we have counted.

Conservation

Conservation of number involves understanding that three is always three, whether it is three objects together, three objects spread apart, or some other formation. As students learn to count, you will see many who do not yet understand this idea. They think that the larger the arrangement of objects, the more objects there are. Being able to conserve quantity is not a skill that can be taught; it is a cognitive process that develops as children grow.

Counting by Groups

Counting a set of objects by equal groups such as 2s, requires that each of the steps mentioned above happens again, at a different level. Students need to know the 2s sequence (2, 4, 6, 8) by rote. They need to realize that one number in this count represents two objects, and that each time they say a number they are adding another group of two to their count. Keeping track while counting by groups becomes a more complex task as well. Students begin to explore counting by groups in the data unit, "Counting Ourselves and Others," as they count the number of eyes in their class. However, most students will not count by groups in a meaningful way until first or second grade.

About Pattern Blocks

Each set of pattern blocks includes 250 blocks in six geometric shapes and colors.

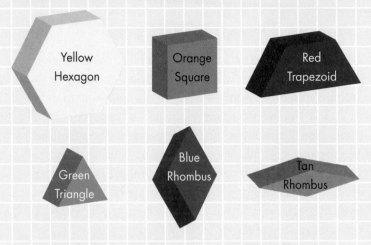

Yellow Hexagon A hexagon is a 6-sided polygon. This block is a regular hexagon because all the sides and angles are equal.

Orange Square A square is a 4-sided polygon with four equal sides and equal angles. A square is also a rectangle.

Red Trapezoid A trapezoid is a 4-sided polygon that has one pair of parallel sides.

Green Triangle A triangle is a 3-sided polygon. This triangle is an equilateral triangle because all of the sides and all of the angles are equal.

Blue Rhombus and Tan Rhombus Both of these rhombuses are parallelograms—4-sided polygons with two pairs of parallel sides. Rhombuses are a special kind of parallelogram; they have four equal sides. You might have noticed that the orange square is also a parallelogram with four equal sides, so it is a rhombus too.

The pattern blocks are related in a variety of ways. Each block, except for the trapezoid, is a regular shape; the length of every side is equal. The trapezoid has one side that is twice as long as the other three. The areas of some of the blocks are also related; the area of the red trapezoid

is half that of the hexagon, the area of the blue rhombus is one third that of the hexagon, and a green triangle is one sixth. Thus, two red trapezoids, three blue rhombuses, and six green triangles all have the same area as a yellow hexagon and can be arranged into shapes that are congruent with the yellow hexagon. Other combinations work similarly, including one red trapezoid and three green triangles; one red trapezoid, one blue rhombus, and one green triangle; two blue rhombuses and two green triangles.

As students explore this material they may begin to notice some of these relationships.

Some kindergarteners may be familiar with the names of some of the pattern block shapes, such as the square and the triangle, but others may not know the names of any of the shapes. Because all pattern blocks of the same color are the same shape, it is very natural for students to identify them by color. This is fine because they are finding ways of identifying and distinguishing the blocks. Begin using the correct geometric terms yourself, and you will find that some students will begin to use them as well. They will have many more opportunities to use and describe these blocks in the geometry unit *Make a Shape, Build a Block*.

Note that although we usually refer to the pattern-block shapes as if they were two-dimensional, they actually have three dimensions. Because the pattern blocks are all the same thickness, most activities involving them focus attention on only one face of the block—the triangle, square, rhombus, trapezoid, or hexagon.

Once students are familiar with the pattern blocks, some may be interested in recording their designs. The easiest way for kindergarters to record designs is with paper pattern blocks, which can be glued onto sheets of paper or cardstock. Use manufactured sets or make your own using Pattern-Block Cutouts (M6–M11). To make your own, copy these shapes on colored paper, ask parent volunteers to help cut them out, and store them in separate plastic bags.

Teacher Note

About Geoblocks

We live in a three-dimensional world, yet most of the geometry students do in school concerns two-dimensional shapes. We frequently use two-dimensional drawings to help us picture and represent three-dimensional things. For example, we use:

- A blueprint to build a house

- A paper pattern to cut out and sew a shirt

- A diagram to assemble a bike

Geoblocks are a special set of three-dimensional wooden blocks. Although similar to other Kindergarten blocks (wooden unit blocks), they are smaller and related by volume. One reason we include Geoblocks in the Kindergarten materials is because it is important for students to work with three-dimensional materials and see the relationship between three- and two-dimensional shapes.

In the *Investigations* curriculum, students use Geoblocks in the Grades K, 1, 2 geometry units. You can make the Geoblocks available to students throughout the year, during indoor recess or a free Math Workshop. Most kindergarteners love to build with these blocks. They build towers, towns, roads, ramps, bridges, and many other things. During this informal building time, they intuitively learn many of the characteristics of the blocks.

Because there are a limited number of Geoblocks, especially some types, sharing is often an issue. There are 128 small cubes, but only two of the largest blocks and only four or six of many of the triangular blocks. To help with sharing, it is a good idea to separate each set of 330 Geoblocks into two or three nearly equal sets. If divided into three sets, there will be enough blocks for two to three students to use at one time. If they are divided into two sets, there will be enough for four to five students to use. Probably the easiest way to divide the main set of blocks is to find two (or three) identical blocks and put one in each set. Parent volunteers, aides, or older student volunteers can do this, although the sorting task is a good way for you to become familiar with the shapes yourself.

Encourage students to use the blocks in just one subset. Before sending students off to explore and build, you might model ways to share blocks, request them, and respond to requests for them. Students need to be able to accept the fact that the block they want may be important in someone else's construction, too. You can encourage students to combine buildings or to build together. See **Teacher Note: Supporting Students' Free Play, page 132.** Finally, students who cannot find the block they want can be encouraged or challenged to find two or more other blocks that combine to make the original. This is a possibility for most blocks in this set, which is one of their useful mathematical attributes.

For your own information, there are five kinds of shapes in the Geoblock set. Before you read these descriptions, we suggest that you do your own sorting of the blocks, because they are probably less familiar to you than some of the other Kindergarten materials. Once you have sorted the blocks into groups that you think go together, the descriptions will probably make more sense. Kindergarteners are not expected to learn the formal names or descriptions of Geoblock shapes.

All the Geoblock shapes are polyhedra—three-dimensional, solid shapes with flat faces. These are the five general categories:

Rectangular Prisms

These prisms have two opposite faces that are the same size and shape (congruent). All other faces that connect these two opposite faces are rectangles. In rectangular prisms the two opposite faces are rectangles, so all six faces are rectangles. You can also call these shapes rectangular solids.

Rectangular prisms

Square Prisms

These are a special kind of rectangular prism. They have two opposite faces that are congruent squares. The other four faces are rectangles.

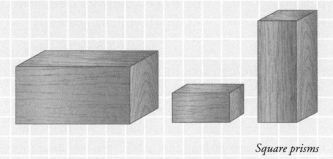

Square prisms

Cubes

Just as the square is a special kind of rectangle, the cube is a special kind of rectangular prism in which all of the faces are squares.

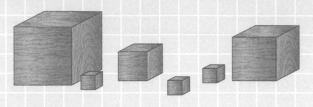

Cubes

Triangular Prisms

These prisms have two opposite faces that are congruent triangles. As in any prism, the faces that connect this pair are all rectangles.

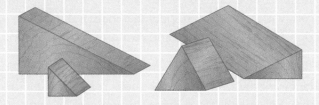

Triangular prisms

Pyramids

There is one kind of pyramid in the Geoblock set. Pyramids look different from prisms. They have one base, which can be any polygon. The rest of the faces are triangles that meet in a single point (vertex). The pyramid in the Geoblock collection is a square pyramid. It has a square base and four triangular faces.

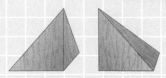

Pyramids

Cube A
1 cm × 1 cm × 1 cm
Quantity: 128

Rectangular prism H
2 cm × 4 cm × 4 cm
Quantity: 12

Triangular prism O
4 cm × 4 cm × 2 cm
Quantity: 12

Triangular prism U
4 cm × 8 cm × 1 cm
Quantity: 6

Cube B
2 cm × 2 cm × 2 cm
Quantity: 32

Rectangular prism I
1 cm × 8 cm × 4 cm
Quantity: 8

Triangular prism P
3 cm × 3 cm × 4 cm
Quantity: 8

Triangular prism V
2 cm × 4 cm × 2 cm
Quantity: 7

Cube C
3 cm × 3 cm × 3 cm
Quantity: 12

Rectangular prism J
2 cm × 8 cm × 4 cm
Quantity: 4

Triangular prism Q
2 cm × 4 cm × 4 cm
Quantity: 2

Triangular prism W
4 cm × 3.5 cm × 2 cm
Quantity: 6

Cube D
4 cm × 4 cm × 4 cm
Quantity: 8

Rectangular prism K
4 cm × 8 cm × 4 cm
Quantity: 2

Triangular prism R
4 cm × 8 cm × 2 cm
Quantity: 6

Triangular prism X
2 cm × 8 cm × 2 cm
Quantity: 6

Rectangular prism E
2 cm × 4 cm × 2 cm
Quantity: 8

Triangular prism L
2 cm × 2 cm × 2 cm
Quantity: 32

Triangular prism S
2 cm × 8 cm × 4 cm
Quantity: 6

Square pyramid Y
4 cm × 4 cm × 4 cm
Quantity: 6

Rectangular prism F
2 cm × 6 cm × 2 cm
Quantity: 4

Triangular prism M
4 cm × 4 cm × 4 cm
Quantity: 6

Triangular prism T
2 cm × 4 cm × 8 cm
Quantity: 6

Rectangular prism G
2 cm × 8 cm × 2 cm
Quantity: 4

Triangular prism N
4 cm × 8 cm × 4 cm
Quantity: 2

Supporting Students' Free Play

When students are first introduced to manipulatives, they make a wide variety of choices about how to use them. Many students dive right in and are able to set themselves tasks and successfully create something with which they are pleased. Others, however, need some support and structure to help them take their first steps. When students are hesitant, help them notice what their classmates are doing. You might encourage any of the following common approaches.

Accumulating Lots of Blocks or Cubes

Young students love to accumulate things. One way to take advantage of this is to enclose a space in some way and then have students collect other blocks inside the enclosure. Students might describe their work in the following ways.

This is the treasure room and these are the treasures.

This is a junkyard and this is where they store the tires, this is where they have things that don't work anymore, and these are the flags that are hung up.

Students like to make long trains or snakes or tall towers with the connecting cubes. Counting can come up with any of the materials, but it is especially likely with the connecting cubes. Types of questions like the ones below can lead to a focus on counting.

- How tall can you make it before it breaks?

- Can you make a train that is as long as the table?

- How many cubes did you use?

Making Buildings

Sometimes students will start with an idea, such as "I'm going to build a castle," and carry it through. At other times, they will just start building and then notice that their construction reminds them of something. For example, "It looks like a house. Now I'm going to make the driveway."

Sometimes students working independently will connect their separate buildings into one structure and might say something like, "I made this part and Hugo made this part, and we decided to put it together. This part is the museum, and this part is the living room, and the rest is everything else." Encouraging this kind of connecting of separate structures can also help when you are dealing with limited quantities of materials.

During free play students will construct a variety of shapes.

Making Patterns

Pattern blocks, with their built-in geometric relationships, naturally lead to making pattern sequences or symmetrical designs. Some students make flat designs, often working outward from a central hexagon or creating figures like flowers or animals. Others use pattern blocks on their edges to make a wall in a certain pattern; for example, hexagon, triangle, hexagon, triangle, hexagon, and triangle.

Starting with a hexagon is something you might suggest to students who are stuck. Making a wall around a "garden"—this could be a piece of paper—is another possibility to suggest. Some students will become intrigued with creating symmetrical or balanced designs. This is a good opportunity to introduce the idea of symmetry. You might say, "Your design is symmetrical. It's the same on this side and on this side."

Sharing Good Ideas

It is impossible to predict what will come up in your class, but be alert to ideas from your students that others in the class might enjoy. Sometimes these ideas sweep through the class without any help from you. For example, in one class a student started using the connecting cubes to make her initials. Soon other children were trying to make their own initials. The teacher engaged them in conversation about which letters were difficult and why. In another classroom, students (and the teacher) became intrigued with the ways they could balance some of the Geoblocks on others.

Establishing Constraints

You can help some students get started by setting them to a small problem with some constraint. You can suggest that they use a certain number of blocks or cubes to make something. For example, "Make a design with 12 pattern blocks or a building with 20 Geoblocks."

Using paper as a mat helps students contain their work and limits the number of blocks or cubes a single student can use.

One focus of this unit is to introduce students to many of the materials that they will be using throughout the year in math class. As students explore these materials, they informally come to know some of their important attributes. They can then draw on this knowledge when they are asked to use the materials in a more formal way in later units.

Exploring Materials: Introducing Math Vocabulary

As you observe students working with pattern blocks and Geoblocks, you can learn a lot about what they notice about two- and three-dimensional shapes, such as the characteristics they attend to, the relationships they recognize, and the distinctions they make. You might hear students say things like this:

- *Hand me that little square block.*

- *I'm using diamonds all around the edge.*

- *I need more yellow ones.*

- *We need two more of those big long ones.*

- *I need to find another roof one.*

At this age, students will not use many conventional mathematical terms. For example, they probably will not know that a blue pattern block is a rhombus or parallelogram, but may instead use the everyday term, *diamond.* They are likely to know some geometric names, such as square or even triangle, but they may apply them incorrectly. For example, when using the Geoblocks, they might call a cube a square or call a rectangular prism a box.

Here are a few ways you can introduce conventional mathematical names for two- and three-dimensional shapes so students hear these terms used in context.

Manuel: [working with pattern blocks] Look, three of these blue ones can fit right on top of the yellow one.

Teacher: Manuel noticed that three of the blue rhombuses can fit right on top of the hexagon. Did anyone notice any other pieces that can fit right on the hexagon?

Tammy: [working with Geoblocks] I need more tiny boxes for the top of my castle.

Teacher: Tammy is looking for tiny cubes. See how she's using them on her castle? Does anyone have some of the smallest cubes that Tammy could use?

As you talk with students, help them develop their language by asking questions or making comments that challenge them to be clearer and more precise. For example:

Latoya: [working with Patternblocks] I'm using diamonds all around the edge.

Teacher: Are you using all blue rhombuses or are you going to use some of the tan ones too?

Raul: [working with Geoblocks] I'm using the square ones to build a wall.

Teacher: There are a lot of Geoblocks like that. Are you going to use the tiny cubes or the bigger ones?

Students will begin to describe shapes by identifying attributes and by using correct mathematical vocabulary as they hear the vocabulary used many times correctly in context. Throughout the elementary grades, students will have many experiences in classifying, describing, and defining shapes of both two and three dimensions.

Observing Kindergarteners as They Count

In Kindergarten, you can expect to see a wide range of number skills within your class. Students in the same class can vary considerably in age and in their previous experience with numbers and counting.

Your students will have many opportunities to count and use numbers not only in this unit, but throughout the year. You can learn a great deal about what your students understand by observing them. Listen to students as they talk with one another. Observe them as they count orally, as they count objects, and as they use numerals to record. Ask them about their thinking. You may observe some of the following:

Counting Orally

By the end of the year, most kindergarteners will have learned to rote count to 10 and beyond, with some able to count as high as 100. Many will be able to count orally much higher than they can count objects. Many who have learned the internal counting pattern or sequence (1, 2, 3 . . . 21, 22, 23 . . .), will still find the "bridge" numbers into the next decade (such as 19, 20, or 29, 30) difficult. You may hear children count "twenty-eight, twenty-nine, twenty-ten." Just as the young child who says "I runned away" understands something about the regularities of the English language, the student who says "twenty-ten" understands something about the regularity of the counting numbers. Students gradually learn the bridge numbers as they hear and use the counting sequence.

Counting Quantities

Most kindergarteners end the year with a grasp of *quantities* up to 20 or so. Some students accurately count quantities above 20, while others may not consistently count smaller quantities. Some may be inconsistent and count successfully one time while having difficulty the next.

Even when students can accurately count the objects in a set, they may not know that the last number counted also describes the number of objects in the set. You may observe students who successfully count a set of cubes, but have to go back and recount the set to answer the question, "How many cubes are there?" These students have not yet connected the counting numbers to the quantity of objects in a set. Students develop their understanding of quantity through repeated experiences organizing and counting sets of objects. In Kindergarten, many of the activities that focus on quantity can be adjusted so that students are working at a level of challenge appropriate for them.

Organizing a Count

Some students may be able to count objects they can pick up, move around, and organize with far more accuracy than they can when counting static objects, such as pictures of things on a page. You may observe some students who can count objects correctly when the group is organized for them, but you will see others who have trouble organizing or keeping track of objects themselves. They will need many and varied experiences with counting to develop techniques for counting accurately and for keeping track of what they are counting.

Counting by Writing Numbers

Knowing how to write numerals is not directly related to counting and understanding quantity; however, it is useful for representing a quantity that has been counted. Young students who are learning how to write numerals frequently reverse numbers or digits. Often this is not a mathematical problem but a matter of experience. Students need many opportunities to see how numerals are formed and to practice writing them. They should gain this experience by using numbers to record mathematical information, such as the number of students in school today or the number of objects on a page of a counting book. Numeral formation is related to letter formation; both are important in order to communicate in writing. We recommend that rote practice of numeral writing be part of handwriting instruction rather than mathematics.

Sorting and Identifying Attributes

Sorting and classifying is a central scientific, mathematical, and human activity. Important issues of classification arise in many disciplines.

- How can we classify the books in a library in a systematic and useful way?

- Is this animal a new species, or is it part of a class of animals that has already been identified and described?

As children learn about their world, community, language, and culture, they are developing and organizing categories of information.

- Which foods are fruits?

- Which animals are dogs?

- Which behaviors are accepted at my house, at grandma's house, or in the park?

- Which words can you add *-ed* to indicate past tense?

In mathematics, as in other areas, classification is an important activity. Shapes are classified by particular attributes, such as number of sides or faces and types of angles (e.g., a triangle is a polygon with three sides). Numbers are classified by particular characteristics as well (e.g., a prime number is a number with exactly two factors, 1 and the number itself). Classifications must often be developed for collecting data. For example, for a rating scale of one to five, how is a one defined? How is a five defined?

In the broadest sense, classification is about how things (e.g., people, animals, numbers, shapes, attitudes) are alike or different. Sorting any collection into categories requires attending to certain attributes and ignoring others. It is this skill of focusing on particular attributes to the exclusion of others that primary grade students are learning. For example, in order to identify a shape as a triangle, we attend only to certain characteristics.

- Does it have three sides and three angles?

- Is each side a line segment?

- Is the shape closed (i.e., no breaks or gaps)?

We do not pay attention to the size, color, texture, or orientation of the shape in order to identify it as a triangle. Although what to pay attention to and what to ignore may seem obvious to adults in this instance, the whole idea of classifying by particular attributes is an important new area for young students. They are beginning to learn how to look at only a particular attribute and ignore the rest, rather than look at the overall combination of attributes.

In this unit, as students match buttons or attribute blocks that have the same characteristics and sort attribute blocks, they are beginning to identify attributes of objects and look for ways that objects are the same. At first, this can be a difficult task for students. They may focus on the overall look of objects rather than individual attributes and may group only objects together that are exactly the same. Or, they may pay attention to more obvious attributes, such as color, and have a hard time ignoring these attributes to notice that objects have a common characteristic that is less obvious. Students will have many more opportunities to sort objects and data throughout Kindergarten, and in Grades 1 and 2 as well.

Flowers, Dancers, and Pattern-Block Walls

Students vary in the amount of structure and direction they need as they freely explore materials. Asking questions can be an effective way of guiding and structuring a free exploration experience for some students. This can extend their thinking about a particular material and lead them into new ways of using it. In addition, when students work with a partner or small group, they benefit from observing how others use materials. Inviting students to share their constructions and designs is a natural way to exchange ideas.

The following dialogue occurred during Session 1.3 as students freely explored several math materials during Math Workshop. The teacher joins a small group of students working with pattern blocks and asks them to tell her about their constructions.

Kaitlyn: I made a flower. See, the yellow one is the middle, and then the flower part is all around with the blue, and then the green triangles are the stem part.

Kaitlyn's Pattern-Block Flower

Lisa: Mine is a person. Here is her hat. It's red. And then she sort of looks like she is dancing because these ones, these blue diamonds, are her legs.

Lisa's Pattern-Block Person

Teacher: Those blue diamonds, or rhombuses, do make it look like she is dancing.

Kaitlyn: And you used green triangles just like I did. But you made her arms, and I made a stem.

Manuel: Stop shaking the table! I don't want my wall to fall down.

Teacher: I see that some of you are laying the pattern blocks flat on the table and some of you are using them to build up. It is harder to keep them in place when they're on their edges the way Manuel has them. Manuel, can you tell me about your wall?

Manuel: Well, it goes yellow, red, yellow, red, yellow, red and then it switches to yellow, blue, yellow, blue. See, they sort of fit together, right next to each other.

Teacher: Yes, I see that the side of the red trapezoid fits right into the side of the yellow hexagon. And the side of the blue rhombus also fits into one side of the yellow hexagon. I wonder what other blocks will fit exactly together so that you can make that kind of wall?

The conversation is interrupted by some commotion at another table. Three students are building elaborate constructions using pattern blocks. Two are being silly, sliding blocks back and forth across the table. The teacher addresses these two students.

Teacher: Dennis and Mia, the other day you were trying to make a design that would cover a piece of drawing paper, but time ran out and you didn't have a chance to do it. Would you be interested in trying to work on that problem now?

Dennis: Yeah, let's do that.

Mia: No, I don't want to. I want to keep doing this. [She slides another block across the table.]

Teacher: Dennis, you can get a piece of paper from the art shelf. Mia, you'll have to make a choice about what you want to do. Sliding blocks is not one of the choices. If you want to use the blocks today, you'll have to use them in a responsible way. If not, you'll have to leave this activity and make a new choice.

The teacher is helping the students learn about the expectations for how they can work with the math materials, as well as trying to learn more about her students by observing them as they work. She helps redirect students to more productive activities and gives one student clear guidelines about the acceptable ways to use the math materials. She asks students to describe how they are using the materials, and asks them questions that encourage them to further investigate ideas that they have already begun to pursue.

I'm Not 8, I'm 5!

During attendance, this class found that 24 students are present. Now they double-check by counting around the circle. When a student is puzzled that his number is different from his age, the teacher helps everyone make sense of what is being counted and what the numbers mean.

Teacher: We found there are 24 children in school today. When we count things, it's a good idea to count again as a way of double-checking. One way to double-check the number of people is by counting off. Here's how it works: The first person will say "one" and the next person will say "two."

Hugo: And the next person will say "three."

Teacher: Yes, the next person will say three and that will tell us that three people have counted so far. Let's try it. Rebecca, you start and be the first one to say a number.

Rebecca: One!

Brad: Two!

Jennifer: Three!

Teacher: So how many people have counted so far? How can we tell?

Rebecca: One, two, three (points to herself and her two neighbors). You just count them.

Teacher: So far, then, three people have counted. Yoshio, you're next.

Yoshio: Four!

Timothy: Five!

Teacher: Now how many people have counted?

A few students call out five.

Lionel: I'm five, too! (He holds up five fingers.)

Teacher: Yes, you are five years old. Lots of people are five in our class. Sometimes numbers tell us how many

years old people are and sometimes they tell us how many of us there are. When Timothy said five, it was because five people counted so far. Let's count them.

The students count from one to five as the teacher points to the first five children in the circle. The next few students continue the count.

Latoya: Six.

Jae: Seven.

Mary: Eight. But I'm not eight, I'm five.

Teacher: Yes, you're five years old too. In fact, how many people are five years old? Lots of people are five years old in our class. Later we can figure out how many. Who can explain to Mary why she said the number eight?

Rebecca: It's because you are eight people. See, I'm one, but I'm really five, too. (She gets up to count each person in the circle.) He's two, and she's three, four, five, six, seven, and you're eight.

At this point the teacher decides to have Rebecca continue to point to students as they say their number. Rebecca is a confident counter and seems to understand the meaning of counting around the circle.

Victor: Twenty-three.

Carmen: Twenty-four.

Rebecca: There are 24 people here.

Counting around the circle was a challenging task for these kindergarteners. Remember that this was their first time doing the activity, and it was also the beginning of the school year. Students become familiar with the mechanics of this routine as it is repeated over time. As they have more experiences with counting groups of people or objects, students begin to make sense of counting and what the numbers in the counting sequence mean.

What's a Calendar?

The following discussion took place in a Kindergarten class during Session 1.3. The monthly calendar in this class was a rectangular board with metal hooks arranged in rows of seven. The date cards for the month of September hung on the board, numbered 1 to 30. Next to this monthly calendar is a 12-month wall calendar opened to the month of September. This teacher started the discussion by finding out what the students already knew about calendars and how they are used.

Teacher: This morning we're going to begin our meeting by talking about our classroom calendar. I was wondering . . . does anyone know what a calendar is for or what a calendar shows?

Jason: It helps you keep track.

Sarah: It's so you don't forget to do something. My dad is always forgetting to do something.

Timothy: Well, mine at home has pages that you rip off it.

Kiyo: There are different kinds, like the kind that has a window on it.

Manuel: It lets you know the day and the months.

Sarah: It's so you don't forget your birthday.

Mary: I would never forget my birthday. Umm, it's June 12. I think.

Rebecca: When you get to the end of a page, you tear it off, and the next one and the next one. It goes and goes.

Teacher: You know a lot of things about calendars. Take a look at our classroom calendar. What to you notice about it?

Latoya: It has cards with numbers on it.

Yoshio: It's blue.

Kiyo: Some of the cards are yellow and some are green.

Teacher: Yes, the green cards are the weekend days, Saturday and Sunday. The yellow cards are the days we usually come to school. These little tags up here tell the names of the days in the week.

Jason: Like Wednesday is today. It has that thing around it.

Teacher: This is the way that we will show what day it is on the calendar, by hanging this TODAY tag on the hook. Today is Wednesday.

Sarah: And today is 13. My brother is 13.

Teacher: Some of you noticed that the calendar has cards with numbers on them. The numbers are for the days in the month. September has 30 days in it. So far, 13 of the days have gone by. Let's count them.

The students in this class are just beginning to explore the calendar and talk about how they will use it in their classroom. They bring with them a variety of experiences with calendars that the teacher can build on to begin work with the class calendar. Today, the teacher simply discusses with the students the structure of the calendar: the days of the week, weekdays vs. weekend, and the numbers of days in the month. In a few days, the students will help place special days on the calendar, figuring out where they belong.

What Do You Notice?

Asking students to explain what a particular survey or graph is about encourages them to interpret the information they have collected. All too often, students lose sight of the meaning of the data collected and simply focus on the data collection process. This class is discussing their responses to *Today's Question:* "Are you a girl or a boy?" (Session 3.1).

Are you a Girl or a Boy?

Girl	Boy

Emma   Abby
Mia
Sarah Latoya
Rebecca Beth
    Mary
Tammy Kaitlyn
Cindy Carmen
	Lionel Hugo
	Brad Timothy
	   Yoshio
	Ricardo Victor
	Manuel
	Jack Raul

Teacher: Let's look at the chart where everyone recorded an answer to the question, "Are you a girl or a boy?" If you are a girl, you wrote your name here. If you are a boy, you wrote your name here. Take a minute to look carefully at our chart. What do you notice?

Lionel: There's lots of names on it.

Manuel: The writing is in black and blue.

Rebecca: This is my name [gets up and points].

Kaitlyn: And this one is my name: K-A-I-T-L-Y-N. Kaitlyn. [She also gets up and points to her name.]

At this point, anticipating a trend, the teacher quickly has all the students acknowledge their names on the chart.

Teacher: Look very carefully at the chart. Using only your eyes, try to find your name. When you see it, raise your hand. [She waits until almost everyone's hand is raised and then helps two students find their names.]

There are lots of names on this chart; in fact, everyone who is here today has his or her name on this chart. Are there other things you notice about the chart?

Carmen: There's more girls than boys.

Hugo: There's lots of letters.

Yoshio: This word [points] says "Boys." I'm in that group.

Timothy: And this word [points] says "Girls," and I'm *not* in that group. [He whispers, "Do you like girls?" to the boy next to him.]

Teacher: Carmen said that there are *more* girls than boys. How can you tell?

Carmen: The girls' line is longer. See, it goes down lower.

Ricardo: You look at the two sides, and the girls have more on their side because it's got more names on it.

Hugo: There is more of the space filled in on the girls' side. You can see it.

Teacher: So you are comparing the girls' side to the boys' side, and the girls' side has more.

Latoya: I know a different way. You can count. There's 1, 2, 3, . . . , 12 girls. There's 1, 2, 3, . . . , 10 boys. And 12 is more than 10.

Teacher: So another way of figuring out which has more is to count and compare the numbers.

By asking students to make observations about the chart, this teacher was able to get a sense of what aspects of the data they noticed. Although some students made observations about the chart that had little or nothing to do with the data, they were accurate observations nonetheless. From previous experience, this teacher knows that students will learn more about looking at data over time and by having repeated opportunities to hear others comment on data that they have collected.

You Could Use Dots

These students are brainstorming ways to record the number of balls in the Counting Jar. As each idea is suggested, the teacher models how to record the information on a new slip of paper and then tapes the slip onto the "Counting Jar" chart.

Teacher: We have counted the balls in three different ways, and each time we figured out that there were seven balls in the jar. Suppose I wanted to write that information on paper. Who has an idea about how I could show that there were 7 balls in the jar?

Kyle: You could just write, "7 balls."

Mia: Yeah, just write a 7.

Teacher: Like this? [She writes, "7 balls," on a slip of paper.] I'm going to write your names on this paper since this was your idea. But I have a question for you. Suppose I didn't know how to write the number 7. How could I find out?

Abby: You could ask me because I know how to write numbers.

Kyle: Me, too!

Teacher: You could ask a friend. Is there another way?

Manuel: You could look right there [points to the number line that wraps around the meeting area]. And find the 7. [He touches each number as he counts.] 1, 2, 3, 4, 5, 6, 7.

Teacher: The number line is a good place to find out how to write numbers. Is there anything else in the classroom that could help you?

Kiyo: The calendar has numbers.

Kaitlyn: The chart has numbers on the bottom.

Teacher: So one way you could write down how many things are in the jar is by using a number. Are there any other ways to show how many? What if you didn't use numbers?

Tammy: You could draw what's in the jar.

Teacher: What would you draw this time?

Tammy: I would draw some balls. Like, you could use dots to show them.

Teacher: So, on another piece of paper, I'll draw some circles to show the balls. And I'll write Tammy's name on the paper to show it was her idea.

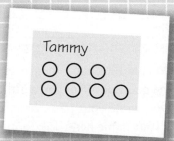

Kaitlyn: You should draw seven of them.

Teacher: Kaitlyn, could you double-check to see whether I have drawn the right number of balls?

Lisa: You could make some lines like this.

Lisa comes to the front of the group and draws lines on a slip of paper. The teacher notices that she has drawn only six lines.

Teacher: Lisa, is there a way that you can double-check your work?

Lisa: Umm, count?

Lisa counts the lines she has drawn and adds one more.

Teacher: Why did you decide to add another line?

Lisa: Because there should be seven lines for seven balls, and I had six lines.

Brad: I have a different way. You could use the stamps and make the number.

Teacher: That's an idea I hadn't thought of. Should I put some of the stamps from the art table next to the Counting Jar? [Students nod.]

Kyle: Well, I'm going to use numbers.

Cindy: I'm going to draw balls, too, like Tammy.

Teacher: Many of you have the same idea about how to show the number of things in the Counting Jar. It's okay to use the same idea. Just be sure your name is on the paper you tape on the chart.

In this discussion, the teacher was able to get a sense of how different students might approach the task. She was particularly interested in Lisa's solution of drawing lines to represent the balls. When she drew only six lines, however, the teacher did not know whether Lisa thought there were six objects in the jar or whether she had miscounted the lines. By asking Lisa to double-check her work, the teacher learned that Lisa had miscounted the lines and was able to correct the information independently.

Student Math Handbook

The *Student Math Handbook Flip Chart* pages related to this unit are pictured on the following pages. This book is designed to be used flexibly: as a resource for providing visual prompts for the teacher to use when introducing a new math activity or idea, as a resource for reviewing math words and ideas with students, and as a resource for students to use as they are doing classwork.

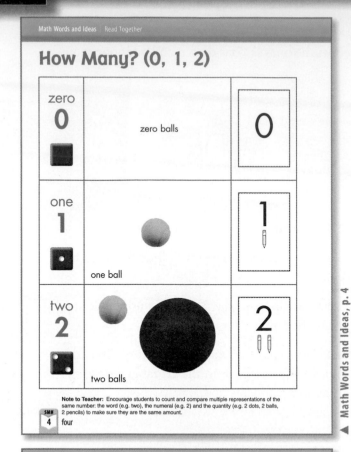

How Many? (0, 1, 2)

zero 0	zero balls	0
one 1	one ball	1
two 2	two balls	2

Note to Teacher: Encourage students to count and compare multiple representations of the same number: the word (e.g. two), the numeral (e.g. 2) and the quantity (e.g. 2 dots, 2 balls, 2 pencils) to make sure they are the same amount.

SMH 4 four

▲ Math Words and Ideas, p. 4

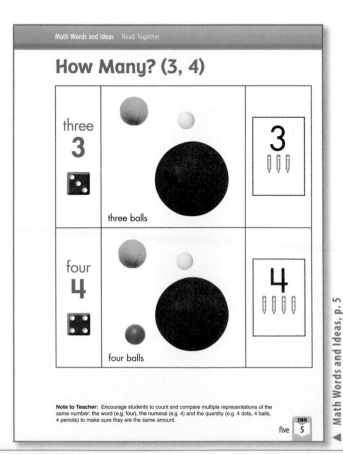

How Many? (3, 4)

| three 3 | three balls | 3 |
| four 4 | four balls | 4 |

Note to Teacher: Encourage students to count and compare multiple representations of the same number: the word (e.g. four), the numeral (e.g. 4) and the quantity (e.g. 4 dots, 4 balls, 4 pencils) to make sure they are the same amount.

five SMH 5

▲ Math Words and Ideas, p. 5

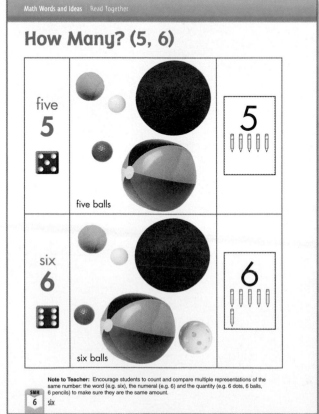

How Many? (5, 6)

| five 5 | five balls | 5 |
| six 6 | six balls | 6 |

Note to Teacher: Encourage students to count and compare multiple representations of the same number: the word (e.g. six), the numeral (e.g. 6) and the quantity (e.g. 6 dots, 6 balls, 6 pencils) to make sure they are the same amount.

SMH 6 six

▲ Math Words and Ideas, p. 6

How Many? (7)

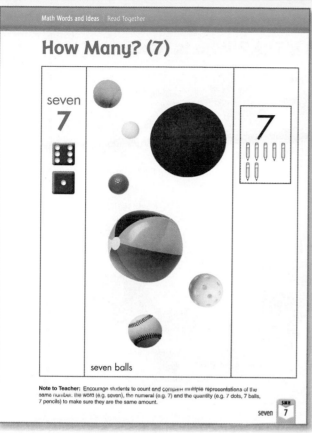

seven
7

seven balls

Note to Teacher: Encourage students to count and compare multiple representations of the same number: the word (e.g. seven), the numeral (e.g. 7) and the quantity (e.g. 7 dots, 7 balls, 7 pencils) to make sure they are the same amount.

SMH
seven 7

▲ Math Words and Ideas, p. 7

How Many? (8)

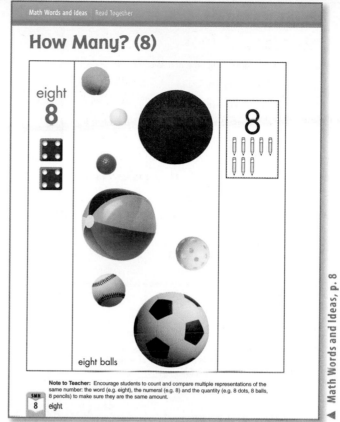

eight
8

eight balls

Note to Teacher: Encourage students to count and compare multiple representations of the same number: the word (e.g. eight), the numeral (e.g. 8) and the quantity (e.g. 8 dots, 8 balls, 8 pencils) to make sure they are the same amount.

SMH
8 eight

▲ Math Words and Ideas, p. 8

How Many? (9)

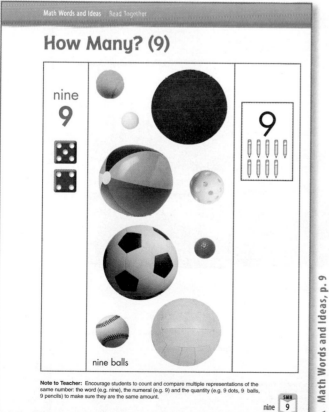

nine
9

nine balls

Note to Teacher: Encourage students to count and compare multiple representations of the same number: the word (e.g. nine), the numeral (e.g. 9) and the quantity (e.g. 9 dots, 9 balls, 9 pencils) to make sure they are the same amount.

SMH
nine 9

▲ Math Words and Ideas, p. 9

How Many? (10)

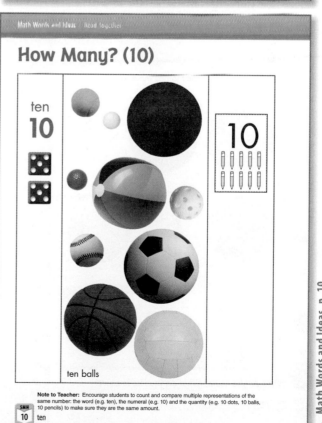

ten
10

ten balls

Note to Teacher: Encourage students to count and compare multiple representations of the same number: the word (e.g. ten), the numeral (e.g. 10) and the quantity (e.g. 10 dots, 10 balls, 10 pencils) to make sure they are the same amount.

SMH
10 ten

▲ Math Words and Ideas, p. 10

Calendar

A **calendar** is a tool for keeping track of time and events.

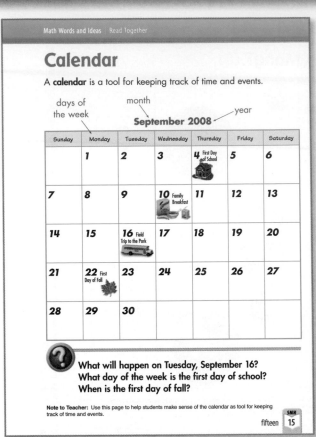

days of the week

month

September 2008

year

Sunday	Monday	Tuesday	Wednesday	Thursday	Friday	Saturday
	1	2	3	4 First Day of School	5	6
7	8	9	10 Family Breakfast	11	12	13
14	15	16 Field Trip to the Park	17	18	19	20
21	22 First Day of Fall	23	24	25	26	27
28	29	30				

What will happen on Tuesday, September 16?
What day of the week is the first day of school?
When is the first day of fall?

Note to Teacher: Use this page to help students make sense of the calendar as tool for keeping track of time and events.

fifteen **15**

Math Words and Ideas, p. 15

Who is First? Who is Next?

tenth, 10th

ninth, 9th

eighth, 8th

seventh, 7th

first, 1st

sixth, 6th

second, 2nd

fifth, 5th

third, 3rd

fourth, 4th

Note to Teacher: When they line up, ask students to use ordinals to identify their position in line (e.g. first, second, etc.).

16 sixteen

Math Words and Ideas, p. 16

Counting

People count every day. They count to find out how many.

How many balls?

1   2   3

4   5   6   7

10 balls

8   9   10

When do you count? What do you like to count?

Note to Teacher: Because counting is the foundation for much of the number work that Kindergarteners do, encourage them to discuss why they count.

seventeen **17**

Math Words and Ideas, p. 17

More Counting

How many students are here today?

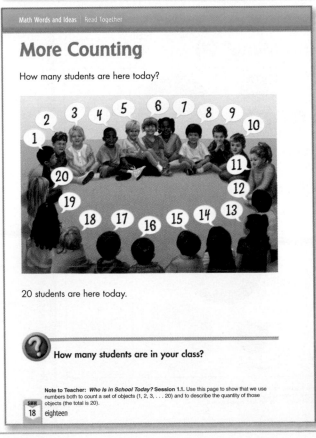

20 students are here today.

How many students are in your class?

Note to Teacher: *Who Is in School Today?* Session 1.1. Use this page to show that we use numbers both to count a set of objects (1, 2, 3, . . . 20) and to describe the quantity of those objects (the total is 20).

18 eighteen

Math Words and Ideas, p. 18

Counting Jar

Math Words and Ideas | Read Together

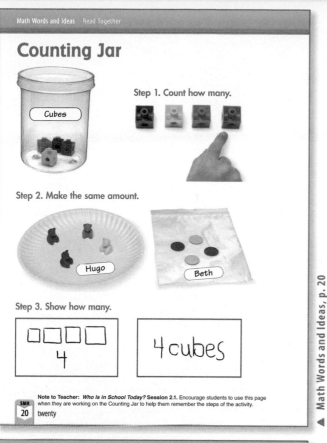

Step 1. Count how many.

Step 2. Make the same amount.

Hugo

Beth

Step 3. Show how many.

4

4 cubes

Note to Teacher: *Who Is in School Today?* **Session 2.1.** Encourage students to use this page when they are working on the Counting Jar to help them remember the steps of the activity.

SMH 20 twenty

▲ Math Words and Ideas, p. 20

Today's Question

Math Words and Ideas | Read Together

Here are some data from a Kindergarten class.

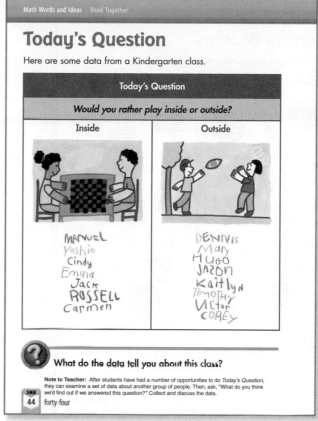

Today's Question

Would you rather play inside or outside?

Inside | Outside

MANUEL
Yoshio
Cindy
Emma
Jack
RUSSELL
Carmen

DENIVIS
Mary
HUGO
JAZON
Kaitlyn
TIMOTHY
VICTOR
COREY

What do the data tell you about this class?

Note to Teacher: After students have had a number of opportunities to do *Today's Question,* they can examine a set of data about another group of people. Then, ask, "What do you think we'd find out if we answered this question?" Collect and discuss the data.

SMH 44 forty-four

▲ Math Words and Ideas, p. 44

Describing Attribute Blocks

Math Words and Ideas | Read Together

These students are describing attribute blocks.

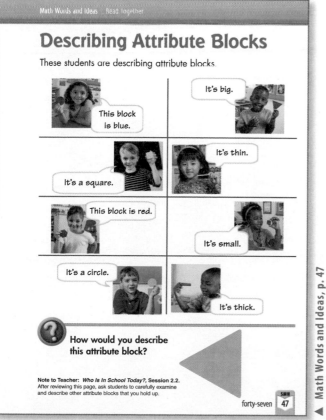

This block is blue.

It's big.

It's a square.

It's thin.

This block is red.

It's small.

It's a circle.

It's thick.

How would you describe this attribute block?

Note to Teacher: *Who Is In School Today?,* **Session 2.2.** After reviewing this page, ask students to carefully examine and describe other attribute blocks that you hold up.

forty-seven SMH 47

▲ Math Words and Ideas, p. 47

Same and Different

Math Words and Ideas | Read Together

Cindy and Hugo compared their bicycles.

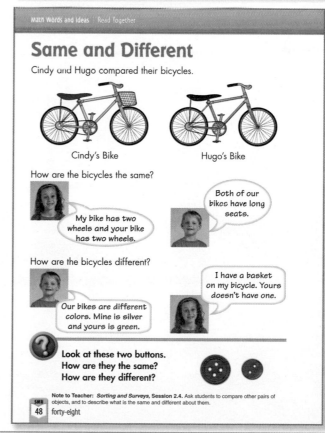

Cindy's Bike

Hugo's Bike

How are the bicycles the same?

My bike has two wheels and your bike has two wheels.

Both of our bikes have long seats.

How are the bicycles different?

Our bikes are different colors. Mine is silver and yours is green.

I have a basket on my bicycle. Yours doesn't have one.

Look at these two buttons. How are they the same? How are they different?

Note to Teacher: *Sorting and Surveys,* **Session 2.4.** Ask students to compare other pairs of objects, and to describe what is the same and different about them.

SMH 48 forty-eight

▲ Math Words and Ideas, p. 48

Sorting Buttons

Timothy sorted these buttons in different ways.

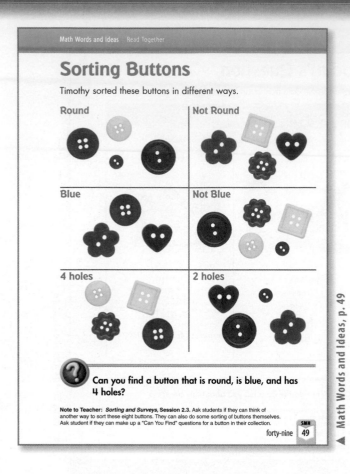

Round

Not Round

Blue

Not Blue

4 holes

2 holes

? Can you find a button that is round, is blue, and has 4 holes?

Note to Teacher: *Sorting and Surveys*, **Session 2.3.** Ask students if they can think of another way to sort these eight buttons. They can also do some sorting of buttons themselves. Ask student if they can make up a "Can You Find" questions for a button in their collection.

forty-nine

SMN
49

◀ Math Words and Ideas, p. 49

Index